THE
POLTERGEIST
EXPERIENCE

THE

POLTERGEIST

EXPERIENCE

Investigations into Ghostly Phenomena

D. SCOTT ROGO

THE AQUARIAN PRESS

This edition published 1990

First published by Penguin Books, 625 Madison Avenue,
New York 10022, USA, 1979

Grateful acknowledgement is made for permission to reprint from the
following: *Ghosts and Poltergeists* by Herbert Thurston; reprinted by
permission of Gateway Editions, Ltd. *The Link* by Matthew Manning;
copyright © Colin Smythe, Ltd., 1974; reprinted by permission of Holt,
Rinehart and Winston, Publishers, and Van Duren, Publishers. *The
Poltergeist* by William G. Roll; copyright © William G. Roll, 1972;
reprinted by arrangement with The New American Library, Inc., New
York, New York.

British Library Cataloguing in Publication Data

Rogo, D. Scott
   The poltergeist experience.
   I. Title
   133.1'4

   ISBN 0-85030-887-9

*The Aquarian Press is part of the Thorsons Publishing Group,
Wellingborough, Northamptonshire, NN8 2RQ, England.*

Printed in Great Britain by Mackays of Chatham, Kent

10 9 8 7 6 5 4 3 2 1

To Raymond Bayless—
  who taught me to appreciate,
  investigate, and revere
  the poltergeist

Contents

Acknowledgments

I would like to thank Mr. Raymond Bayless for turning over to me his notes on several poltergeists. I have drawn frequently on these notes during the writing of this book. Thanks are also due to the Parapsychology Foundation for allowing me to adapt portions of my paper "Demonic Possession and Parapsychology," which appeared in the November/December 1974 issue of *Parapsychology Review;* and to the Society for Psychical Research for allowing me similar use of my paper "Psychotherapy and the Poltergeist," which appeared in the *Journal of the Society for Psychical Research* for September 1974. And of course, special thanks are due to the many families who have invited me into their homes to observe and investigate the poltergeists that were plaguing them.

Foreword

On March 14, 1962, the *Los Angeles Times* ran a short but incredible story. It read in part:

Glassware has been breaking up all over Mrs. Beck's home without apparent cause—one piece even flying around a corner before shattering.

The police are baffled, and their presence doesn't inhibit the poltergeist, or whatever force is moving the glassware around. A policeman was struck on the back Monday by a glass he was investigating.

Mrs. Beck said it started Sunday night when a piece of crystal on top of a bookcase in an upstairs bedroom crashed to the floor almost four feet from the bookcase.

Figurines, ashtrays, vases, goblets, drinking glasses, and other glassware started sailing through the air and smashing.

Mrs. Beck, her daughter, and her mother felt stinging pains in their arms and found small puncture wounds. They said the wounds looked like the bite of a bat.

A friend said he and his wife and Mrs. Beck were sitting in the kitchen when a large glass vessel sailed around a corner and shattered at their feet.

These events were occurring in Indianapolis and creating quite an uproar. Not only were they terrorizing the unfortunate family mentioned in the report, but the police were baffled by them as well.

To many people this report will seem "incredible," since household objects don't normally fly through the air by themselves. Nonetheless literally hundreds of well-documented reports similar to this one have been placed on record. In this case, for instance, so many witnesses observed the flying objects that we know at least *something* very strange was occurring that week in March of 1962.

The poltergeist, which is a term used to denote outbreaks such as these, is one of the most bizarre forms of psychic phenomena. In this book I hope not only to recount many of these cases, but also to explore some of the mechanics behind these phenomena, and to discuss the psychic abilities of the people who seem to be able to produce them. However, this book is not just an armchair study of the poltergeist. Having spent the last twelve years or so of my life as a psychical investigator, I have had the good fortune to investigate several such occurrences. The existence of the poltergeist is something for which I can vouch from firsthand experience.

Although I began my active career in parapsychology in 1966, I did not make my first on-the-spot investigation of an active poltergeist case until 1972. (I had, however, investigated several more conventional "haunted houses" previously.) I did not personally witness any of the phenomena during this investigation. However, in 1974 I was called to investigate an active case brewing in a southern California suburb and during an exciting three-day vigil I observed the poltergeist in action. Needless to say, it made a profound impression on me. Although I had previously studied most of the scientific literature on the poltergeist, actually observing one in action was an experience both intellectually and emotionally striking. In one respect this book is a result of that case, for it prompted me to reevaluate and restudy everything I had ever learned about the phenomena. Since then I have been able to investigate other cases and talk with several poltergeist victims and investigators alike.

This book, therefore, is meant to be not only an introduction to the study of the poltergeist, but also a personal statement about my own investigations (which I will relate during the course of the following chapters) and what I think the poltergeist reveals about our psychic potentials. Perhaps my speculations will strike the reader as a little "offbeat." But then... unconventional phenomena prompt us to think in correspondingly unconventional terms.

The poltergeist is a psychic mystery of the first degree. I hope that in this book I have at least been able to offer a few ideas which might help us to solve this mystery at some point in the future.

The Poltergeist Experience

1

The Hidden Forces of the Mind

The scene is the Division of Parapsychology and Psychophysics at Maimonides Medical Center in Brooklyn, New York. I am sitting before a movie screen next to a young attractive red-haired woman who works in the hematology department upstairs. The lights are lowered and on the screen in front of us I proceed to watch a rather peculiar sight. The film shows the same red-haired girl engaged in a most unusual act. She is staring intently at a small bottle half filled with liquid, which is standing inconspicuously on a kitchen counter. Her arms lie flat on the counter surface on either side of the container, but a good distance from it. Her stares gradually become more and more intense, so intense that her whole body actually begins to quiver. Finally something happens that has major scientific implications: the small bottle begins to slide with little jolts of movement. Now, there are no strings attached to the bottle, and the camera is close enough to expose any indication if the young woman were blowing or pushing the bottle. The counter is absolutely level, and the subject is moving the bottle by the sheer psychic force of her will and, in fact, continues to move it for several inches.

This film might unnerve anyone unfamiliar with the mysteries of psychic phenomena. However, tales of people who can levitate tables, move objects by willpower alone, and even lift themselves into the air are as old as humankind. And, perhaps more startling, some of these tales have turned out to be more than just supernatural legend. Today, as the study of psychic phenomena is rapidly gaining scientific acceptance and even guarded support, researchers from every conceivable science—biology, physics, psychology, and even anthropology—are beginning to study such phenomena as ESP, mind over matter, out-of-body travel, and a host of other unusual occurrences or talents with all the technology available to them. And in this super-jet-age era, when science and technology are making some of their greatest strides, a few gifted psychics have been demonstrating these legendary "mind-over-matter" abilities in some of the most prestigious scientific laboratories of the world.

Probably the most famous of these psychics is a middle-aged Russian housewife named Nina Kulagina, whose psychokinesis (or PK for short, which literally means "to move by the mind") has been studied by dozens of scientists from the U.S.S.R., the United States, England, and Australia. At the present time, at least two dozen detailed films have been made of her ability to move small objects just by concentrating on them. Kulagina is one of modern science's greatest puzzles.

Her abilities were first discovered by L. L. Vasiliev, a Soviet parapsychologist, sometime in the 1960s. At the time he was engaged in several ESP experiments as part of his work as head of the Leningrad-based Institute for Brain Research. For one of his many projects, Vasiliev was endeavoring to determine whether or not he could "train" people to sense the color of objects merely by touching them. One of his subjects, Nina Kulagina, seemed particularly gifted with this ability, so Vasiliev decided to see how well she could develop the ability with training. The research was going well until, one day, Vasiliev noted something quite unusual about his subject's performance. Sometimes as she moved her hands over an object without touching it, it would move slightly.

Vasiliev immediately realized that he had discovered a psychic talent much more powerful than he had at first thought, and soon found that Kulagina could deflect a compass by waving her hand over it and, by an incredible force of will and physical strain, could psychically push small household objects about a table. She could, for instance, slide vials across a tabletop, or make one specific match lodged in a pile detach itself and move away from the others. She could even move objects placed under plastic or glass containers. Unfortunately Vasiliev died in 1966, but since then dozens of other Iron Curtain scientists have been able to work with Kulagina with exceptional results. Several Western scientists have been allowed by Soviet authorities to test and experiment with her as well.

One important report on Kulagina's PK power, written when scientists in the United States and Western Europe were first beginning to hear about this Soviet wonder, was presented by Leo Kolodny, a *Pravda* reporter, who visited the Russian housewife hoping to expose the whole affair as a cheap sham. He was in for quite a surprise, though, as he explained in his report on her, which appeared in a March 1968 issue of *Pravda*. In order to test the psychic's supposed abilities, Kolodny simply removed the cap of his pen and placed it on a table in the psychic's apartments. Kulagina was up for the challenge and, seating herself beside the table, began concentrating on the small object. Kolodny busied himself by writing notes on the experiment, while keeping his eyes on the psychic and cap simultaneously: "I write and at the same time I glance at the cap. I write until the pen drops from my hand in amazement; the cap creeps along the tablecloth. At first it makes a sharp jerk, another jerk, and crawls toward the very edge of the table. Behind it crawls the neighboring tumbler, as if they were hauled in one and the same harness. . . ."

In order to test the psychic further, Kolodny placed a glass over the pen cap, whereupon the little piece of plastic acted like a trapped insect. To his surprise it meandered back and forth under the barrier, bumping into the glass wall.

Kolodny returned to the Kulagina home the next day. Since he hoped to film the PK, he brought along two cameras and five cameramen. Kulagina began the day's demonstration by using her PK to deflect a compass needle. This is one of her most famous feats, and the cameras were there to record every second of it. As usual, Kulagina sat at a table in full view for the duration of the experiment. As Kolodny reported to *Pravda*:

The room was crowded with two cine-cameras and five cameramen. We take the table-cloth off the table, remove everything unnecessary, leaving in front of the lens only a traveller's compass on a leather strap. The pointer is motionless. Then after about twenty minutes' effort from Kulagina it vacillates, swings and makes a half-revolution. But this is not enough. The pointer could waver simply from an imperceptible shaking of the table. And then Kulagina—at the cost of tremendous effort—in the sight of the amazed cameramen operating their whirring cameras, makes the pointer revolve on its axis, as if in front of her is not the pointer of a compass, but the second hand of a watch. At first I have time to count the number of revolutions: two...three...four ...and already it becomes difficult to count: the pointer of the compass spins like a top!

It spun like a top and the compass in a plastic case with a leather strap spun by itself in the very center of the table, sweeping aside all suspicions that the pointer was turned by a magnet concealed somewhere. Is it possible to turn the plastic body of the compass with such a magnet? From the compass Kulagina transferred her gaze to the objects standing side by side under a plastic cover: a strap, a matchbox and scattered matches. They all—the matchbox, strap, and matches— move to the edge of the table, sweeping away as they go all suspicion of an invisible thread. Coult it be possible to tie together ten matches with a matchbox and strap, in such a way that they moved independently of one another!

After the experiment was over, Kulagina treated her skeptical guests to an encore. With the bravado of a seasoned performer, she grabbed everything in sight— matches, a fountain pen cap, a small plastic box, and even an apple—and placed them on the table before her. Within moments all the objects crawled toward her as though animated, and the apple and matches fell off the end of the table.

By 1968, the year of Kolodny's *Pravda* report, so many scientists had witnessed Kulagina's PK that Dr. Zdenek Rejdak, a Czech scientist who has studied her in depth, organized a conference on parapsychology in Prague. Several presentations were made about Kulagina at this meeting and several films depicting her psychic talents at work were shown to the scientific community at large. These films made a great impact not only in Czechoslovakia, but eventually in the West as well, since several of them were carefully smuggled out of the U.S.S.R.

Could the Soviet films be fakes? This was the key question that scientists in America began to address. In hopes of finding an answer, two American parapsychologists, J. G. Pratt of the University of Virginia and Dr. Montague Ullman of Maimonides Medical Center in Brooklyn, independently traveled to the Soviet Union in order to witness Kulagina's abilities for themselves. Both of them came back impressed. Ullman, in fact, even presented films showing Kulagina's PK at work to the staff of the Maimonides Medical Center's Division of Parapsychology. (This laboratory is one of the top parapsychology centers in the United States.) This screening, however, was to prove more significant than Ullman had dreamed. His motivation for showing the footage was simply to give the lab staff a chance to see motion pictures of PK actually moving stationary objects. After all, PK on stationary objects is one of the rarest forms of psychic ability known to science. But the upshot of this screening, which was held in 1971, opened a new chapter in science's quest to understand PK.

In the audience that day was a young hematologist named Felicia Parise, who worked at the hospital and who was also one of the Division of Parapsychology's best ESP subjects. Felicia became obsessed with the films and decided that with practice she could develop similar abilities. And she was right. After weeks of practice with a small vial, Felicia finally succeeded in moving it. By concentrating on the object until she literally lost all contact with exterior reality, she could make it move in little spurts. No physical or electrostatic force could explain these motions, and soon Felicia became one of the most important subjects in contemporary parapsychology. Now American parapsychologists had a Kulagina of their own.

At first she was tested at Maimonides Medical Center by Charles Honorton, director of research at the center's parapsychology division, who proved that she could move objects even when they were placed under a fraud-proof bell jar. As he reported to the 1973 Convention of the Parapsychological Association:

Late in the summer of 1971, while in Durham, North Carolina, I received a letter from Parise in which she reported success in displacing a small alcohol bottle, presumably by PK. When I returned to New York I was invited to her home for a demonstration. The alcohol bottle was actually a small clear plastic medicine bottle (59 mm. high and 34 mm. in diameter), filled approximately one-fourth with denatured alcohol. Parise used this bottle to preserve her cosmetic eyelashes. As we arrived in the kitchen, she placed the bottle on the formica countertop, approximately one foot back from the edge of the counter. She placed her hands on the edge of the counter, then silently looked at the bottle for two to three minutes. At that point she exclaimed that the bottle had moved. I did not see any movement. Parise was silent for another minute or two. Then the bottle moved one and one-half to two inches to my right and away from her. I then picked up the bottle and examined it carefully to be sure that there was no moisture present and nothing attached to it, then replaced it on the counter to see if it would slide by itself. The bottle did not move. Later, Parise again placed her fingers on the edge of the counter. This time the bottle began slowly to move forward and to my right, in a curved trajectory. It stopped and started again three times and finally (after reaching a distance of approximately four and one-half inches from its starting position) reversed direction, returning toward me, and then stopped.

The stopping-starting-reversing behavior of the bottle did not fit well with my sliding hypothesis. I spent more than half an hour examining the counter, drawers, etc., and became pretty well acquainted with Parise's kitchen. I attempted to repeat the movements through a variety of normal means. I tried pressing gently and firmly against the sides, top, and underside of the counter; I forcibly jarred the countertop; I moistened the counter and the bottle by spilling some of the alcohol solution. I was completely unsuccessful at getting the bottle to move. Later, I took a carpenter's level to her counter and found that it was in fact not perfectly level, it inclined slightly to the right. The bottle had apparently been moving into the incline. During the following months I had occasion to repeat these observations, under the same conditions, a number of times. Parise became successful at deflecting the needle of a small pocket compass. In working with the compass, she would frequently place her hands, cupped slightly, a la Kulagina, around the periphery of the compass, about six inches over its surface. Often I would unexpectedly pass her hands directly over the surface of the compass to insure against concealed metallic shavings, etc. In no case did similar movements occur when I did this.

Later these effects were filmed. (This was the film I described at the beginning of the chapter.)

As a next step in his research, Honorton took Felicia to the Institute for Parapsychology of the Foundation for Research on the Nature of Man. (This was originally the Duke Parapsychology Laboratory, which was reorganized off campus after J.B. Rhine, its founder, retired from the university.) There, outside investigators also tested Felicia successfully, and made an even more interesting discovery about her PK. Graham and Anita

Watkins, two research associates at the lab, were interested in seeing if Felicia's PK could set up some sort of force-field. Indeed, they were able to demonstrate that if she used PK to deflect a compass in a certain area of the lab, the compass would continue to deflect if brought back to the same area even if Felicia was no longer exerting her PK. This would also occur if she left the area. The effect lasted about thirty minutes before dissipating.

Although Felicia's PK usually manifested itself when she willed it, at times it would occur spontaneously. Honorton himself once witnessed such an occurrence, which he reported to the 1973 annual meeting of the Parapsychology Association held in Charlottesville, Virginia:

On one occasion, while she [Felicia] was in my office, I tried to coax her to "zap" [deflect] my own compass. She was in a hurry to leave and did not want to get worked up for PK. However I prodded her, and as she stood about 18 inches from the desk on which the compass lay, she waved her arm in the direction and jokingly said, "Abracadabra." The compass needle immediately deflected 90 degrees....

Although I know Felicia well, I have never seen her PK at work. As she told me, her PK eventually became too much of a strain for her physically and psychologically and she didn't want to become chained to constant practice. PK, she explained, is like musical talent. It must be practiced slavishly and she wasn't ready to make that sort of commitment. She also seemed to lose control of her ability, and sometimes objects would spontaneously fly about or topple from the shelves in her presence.

These incidents, which were a constant annoyance to her, usually occurred at her home. Although these occurrences were not frequent, they happened often enough to make her decide that, in order to control the force she had liberated, she must not employ it experimentally but coerce it back into dormancy. However, when I later asked Felicia if she felt she still had her PK ability, she looked at me with a grin and said, "I know it's still there... inside."

Despite the fact that I have never observed Felicia's PK, I have witnessed her remarkable ESP ability, which I was able to study during one of my trips to the Maimonides Medical Center. (In one respect Felicia's ESP has an intricate bearing on the nature of PK. This is a theme to which I will return later.) I ran one experiment with her in February 1975 with amazing results.

For this brief test I placed her in a soundproof booth and asked her to stare into a red light through translucent hemispheres, which I placed over her eyes. At the same time I had her listen to monotonous white noise over headphones. (When subjected to this condition of partial sensory deprivation, volunteer subjects often report that mental images will form against the blank background. These images are similar to the type that occurs just as one drops off to sleep.) After I left the booth Felicia sat and reported her mental images over an intercom to an experimenter who sat in the next room monitoring the equipment.

I stationed myself two rooms away. Before me were over 100 Viewmaster reels, one of which I randomly chose as the target for the test. The reel was titled *Probing the Past* and the first scene depicted an old Roman villa with ruined marble fountains. A speaker was positioned beside me so that I could hear what Felicia was reporting from her station in the lab. Immediately after she had reported her first mental image, I picked up the Viewmaster reel and looked at it for the first time. As I looked at the picture, Felicia's loud and cheery voice came over the intercom. At first she talked about a similar experiment run at the lab, which a Canadian film company had recorded live. The subject of that experiment had been Ellen Messer, another lab volunteer who had successfully described the target reel using only her telepathic ability. The target chosen for her test had been *Las Vegas Strip* and Ellen specifically mentioned seeing images of Las Vegas while in the isolation booth. Felicia chatted on about Ellen's ESP ability and her previous success in the isolation booth, and then said:

"[I]...started thinking about Ellen's hit of Las Vegas. What a marvelous hit in Ellen's film. I remember the Stardust. I remember it from when I was there too....Some imagery, not so much waterfall but fountains, water squirting up, coming down. Caesar's Palace had fountains like that. Roman fountains in white stone or marble."

Felicia had obviously described the target I had selected. Her descriptions of the Roman marble fountains were uncannily accurate. After this experiment was over, I showed Felicia four unrelated reels and asked her to identify the one I had used during the test. She had no difficulty in selecting the correct one.

So just what is the significance of Felicia's psychic abilities? Actually, they tell us a great many things about the nature of people and their relationship to the physical world.

First, the existence of ESP indicates that the human

mind can directly interact with physical matter and gain information from it. In our test together, for instance, Felicia somehow interacted with either the target reel or my brain and picked up enough information from either source to describe the picture. Furthermore, the existence of PK demonstrates not only that the mind can interact with matter but can actually manipulate it as well. It is not odd that subjects who do well on ESP tests often possess PK ability as well. Both faculties demonstrate that a human being can make contact with the outside world in more ways than our sense perceptions would lead us to believe. In fact there is growing evidence that many of us, who do not normally think of ourselves as being in any way psychic, do interact psychically with our environment even though we are unaware of it. It may be that we use these powers so subtly that they go unnoticed until we try to demonstrate them experimentally. Let me cite an example:

During one of my frequent trips to the Maimonides Center I met a young physicist who had just developed a rather complex machine, which he felt could be easily manipulated by PK. Inside the machine is an oscillator-like device that flips back and forth between an "on" and "off" position. This machine oscillates back and forth randomly, so that in ten trials (or coin-flips) it may come up "on" seven times and "off" three times. But over a period of several trials, the machine will generate "on" 50 percent of the time and "off" 50 percent of the time. In order to test for PK, the subject is instructed to try to make the machine generate more "ons" or "offs" than chance could account for.

The subject is placed in an adjoining room, and earphones are placed over his or her ears while the person listens to white noise. (White noise sounds like the static on a radio set tuned in between stations.) The noise is actually generated by the machine and it will stay on as long as the machine generates "ons," and will go off when the machine generates "offs." The rate of the oscillation can be set at any speed. For instance, it might be set to generate 500 trials in one minute, during which time the machine will generate approximately 250 "ons" and 250 "offs." The subject, in order to keep the white noise on as long as possible, must use his or her PK to generate more "ons" than "offs."

I often toyed with this machine during my stay at Maimonides and I proved to my own satisfaction that it did indeed average fifty percent "ons" per series. However, many people have actually been able to make the machine depart from randomness and produce more "ons" and "offs" than chance could account for. Many of these subjects—among them lab volunteers, casual visitors to the lab, and even news reporters—aren't (or don't consider themselves to be) gifted psychics.

During one experiment I watched a volunteer subject "will" the machine to the "on" position about 55 percent of the time. This subject was equally facile in obtaining "offs" 55 percent of the time when instructed to do so. Chance just cannot explain outcomes such as these, especially since the subject was able to produce them repeatedly.

Sharon Harper, one of the Maimonides volunteer research associates, was consistently successful at employing PK during these informal tests. However, when I spoke to her about her abilities, it became clear to me that she was really not aware just *how* she was able to produce these effects. She told me that she merely willed with all her might for the white noise to stay on, and held her breath and tensed her muscles as she concentrated.

Sharon is not as talented as Felicia. Nonetheless she seems to be endowed with the same type of psychic ability that Felicia possesses, but to a lesser degree.

Many people seem to have Sharon's ability to demonstrate very marginal PK effects. Even I have to admit to a little ability myself. For example, if I become elated my wristwatch will often start running fast, about five minutes ahead of time a day. If I get depressed it will begin to run slow, also about five minutes a day. I have observed this phenomenon over a period of years and it seems to be some minor form of PK. I can certainly think of no other explanation for this fluctuation. Probably all of us have some PK potential, but rarely notice it simply because the effects are so insignificant. For years J. B. Rhine and others at Duke University, as well as researchers elsewhere, found that many individuals, who did not otherwise consider themselves in any way psychic, could use PK to make a die land on a designated side more often than chance could account for.

Even though many people can produce a modest amount of PK, under certain conditions it seems likely that one might be able to produce larger-scale PK effects. For example, PK commonly occurs during times of crisis, and for years parapsychologists have collected cases of spontaneous PK, such as clock-stoppings or inexplicable noises, which were witnessed at the time somebody known to the observer had died. Camille Flammarion, a famous French astronomer at the turn of the twentieth century, reported several such cases in his three-volume study of psychic phenomena, *Death and Its Mystery*. The following is typical of the cases he collected:

Two leagues from our home lived an old great-aunt of ours, who was ill. One night at two o'clock in the morning a *terrible noise* suddenly made itself heard on the stairs (of our home) which led from the first floor to the second. It was as if the heavy chest at the head of the stairs had been *thrown from the top to the bottom of this stairway!* My sisters, who slept in different rooms, on the first and second floors, awakened, very much frightened. Trembling, they turned on the lights, and went to the head of the stairs to see what had happened. They saw nothing unnatural. Everything was in its place; no piece of furniture had been disturbed. The next day, at seven o'clock, they came to tell us that *our aunt had died at two o'clock in the morning.*

Sometimes, though, the PK will actually move, break, or throw an object. These outbursts are often related to a death, as in the following case also recorded by Flammarion:

My mother at that time was very unwell. One night the bell—the cord from which ... went from the alcove where my parents slept to the nurse's room on the first floor—this bell, as I was saying, began to ring loudly. In all my haste I, whose room was next to that of the nurse, went to look for the latter, and why the bell had rung. My father and mother told them that they had been dreaming and that no one had rung. At that very moment they heard the bell ring again. My father sprang from his bed. The bell-cord and the clapper were still in motion. ... There were, then, four witnesses, fully awake, and nothing could set the bell in motion save some one in the alcove. Then things resumed their natural course. Before going back to bed my father looked at the clock: it was half past two. The night following the next, he got a letter from Paris, telling him of the death of a relative.

Cases such as these prompt us to ask many questions about spontaneous PK. When the incident cited above took place, for instance, just whose PK caused it? Was it the dying relative's or the onlooker's? There is no clear way to resolve this enigma. However, it is very likely that one of the onlookers might have received an unconscious ESP impression about the death and used PK (still unconsciously) to try to bring the impression to his full attention.

As I said, in these cases the PK is probably being projected by one of the witnesses. One incident witnessed and reported by C. G. Jung, the famous psychoanalyst and one of Freud's first disciples, is typical of this type of PK.

In his autobiographical *Memories, Dreams, Reflections*, Jung reports how he was arguing over the existence and importance of the occult with his great mentor. Freud eschewed the idea that psychic phenomena existed. (Years later he changed his opinion.) During the argument, a loud blow resounded from a bookshelf nearby. Jung, who immediately preceding the event had felt an intense heat in his diaphragm, instantly shouted, "There, that is an example of so-called catalytic exteriorization phenomena." So loud was the crash that both men had risen from their seats fearing the shelf would topple upon them. Freud's pessimism was unflinching. "Oh, come, that is sheer bosh," he retorted. Jung was just as unwavering. "It is not. You are mistaken, Herr Professor," he declared. "And to prove my point, I now predict that in a moment there will be another such loud report." Jung's prediction was correct. As soon as the words had flowed from his mouth, another exploding sound emanated from the bookshelf.

The incident deeply disturbed Freud and, in fact, he never discussed it face to face with Jung afterward. Jung wrote that Freud only looked at him aghast, shaken by what he had witnessed. There can be little doubt that Jung himself projected the PK as a dramatic illustration of the very issue he was championing. Later Freud wrote Jung and accused him of having perpetrated a hoax.

Nonetheless many of us tend to rationalize incidents such as these away. If you were to see an object move by itself it would be easier to rationalize that the incident is due to an earth tremor than accept that something psychic is taking place. I have confronted the paranormal many times during my investigations of hauntings, poltergeists, and psychics—yet even I am not immune to this natural defense. Often after observing a striking incident of PK I will keep going over it in my mind, continually questioning, "Now did I really see and hear what I thought I did?" And days later, after the initial awe has worn off, my tendency toward self-examination leads to even more self-questioning.

The existence of PK seems so incredible that it is often hard to determine whether or not some physical phenomena are due to PK or to some physical force. For example, one evening I was writing at my desk about a "haunted house" I had recently investigated. I had been especially intrigued by a loud detonation-like noise that had occurred in the house during my on-the-spot investigation, and was trying to emphasize in my written report how unbelievably loud the blow was. I had just written that the noise "sounded like a sledge hammer blow." No sooner had I placed the period at the end of the sentence than I heard an unnervingly loud "pop" issue from a large antique wooden buffet in the adjoining dining room. The rap was so loud that I was truly startled. I had heard the buffet creak before but this was of a loudness and intensity beyond anything I have ever heard emanating from it before (or since).

Someone less familiar with paranormal phenomena might simply attribute this pop to a freak thermal creak produced by the antique wood. I certainly would not blame the skeptic for promoting this argument. But the timing was a little *too* perfect and the noise was a little *too* loud. Could it have been caused by PK? My colleague Raymond Bayless offered a novel explanation when I recounted this incident to him. He suggested that a weakness was already present in the buffet's wood, which was very likely to emit a thermal creak at any moment. My PK did not actually produce the blow, but instead catalyzed, activated, and intensified it. In other words, the PK took the path of least resistance. Thus, in his opinion, the pop was both normal and paranormal at the same time.

All of these examples—Felicia's bottle-sliding and compass-deflecting PK; Sharon's ability to offset a high-speed generator; death coincidences; Jung's unconsciously projected PK—represent varieties of one universal ability that has long been one of our organism's most baffling mysteries.

Now just what *is* the basic nature of PK? Is it something for us to use, to exhibit voluntarily, or to harness? Or are those actually artificial manifestations of PK? Could it be that the PK force is meant to work undercover, secretly manipulating our environment?

I am afraid that we just don't know. If anything, parapsychology has more questions than answers about psychic phenomena. It is true, though, that some psychics can "will" spectacular PK feats to take place. Some do it with no conscious physical strain, while others must struggle to free the PK forces within them. The famous Polish psychic Stephan Ossowiecki once was able to make a large heavy rock creep along the floor just by intense concentration alone. The great Italian medium Eusapia Palladino could make tables levitate or cause heavy couches to slide several inches over the floor during perfectly controlled scientific tests.

Yet unconsciously mediated death coincidences are just as awesome and often every bit as spectacular. Yet one common principle does unite these two different expressions of PK power. Just as most of us are not aware how to produce or use PK, even gifted PK subjects cannot systematically control or exhibit their abilities. For instance, Felicia Parise, in the throes of her muscle tension and intense concentration, often failed to slide her light bottle even one centimeter.

And since PK cannot be completely controlled, can a person virtually lose control of PK to such a degree that it begins to run rampant? Just what *would* happen if the full potential of someone's PK suddenly became liberated from his or her mind and body?

These questions are not rhetorical and deserve answering. And here I *can* give an answer: there are such cases on record, during which the mind lets loose an incredible force, which throws objects around, breaks crockery, pounds walls, and even sets fires. This horrendous PK manifestation is what we call the "poltergeist." Translated from the German, the term means "noisy ghost." This phenomenon has plagued humankind around the globe for hundreds of years. Actually, though, the term "poltergeist" is a misnomer, since our own minds—and not ghosts or spirits of the dead—are the true perpetrators of these happenings.

Poltergeist cases are not uncommon, and several are reported by the news media annually. During a typical case the victimized family will be plagued by many types of PK phenomena. Objects will simply fly around their home by themselves. Bangs and crashes will resound from the walls of their house. Victimized families will also sometimes report how household objects continually disappeared, only to fall mysteriously from the ceiling days later as though materialized out of thin air. Naturally the family will first seek a mundane cause for the phenomena. And sometimes there *is* a person behind it all. Children are usually the first to be eyed with suspicion. However, let me say unequivocally that sometimes these outbreaks are genuinely psychic in nature and have been observed by trained scientific investigators.

The poltergeist is no harmless, playful ghost, as its name might lead you to believe. It can be a vicious attacker whose malevolence is only matched by its destructiveness. When the poltergeist erupts, literally all hell breaks loose. Luckily, though, poltergeists are usually short-lived and commonly focus upon only one member of the plagued family, usually a child. It is this person whose PK ability has apparently become unleashed. But there is an issue more important than merely verifying the existence of the poltergeist. This is simply: what exactly is the poltergeist trying to express? Jung's PK apparently manifested itself to augment dramatically a highly emotional argument. Death-coincidence PK occurs in order to announce the death of a relative or friend known to the witness. PK does not occur randomly. When it occurs it does so for a reason. It is for us to fathom that reason. From whom does the PK emanate? What is it trying to express? And how does it express itself? These are the true mysteries behind the poltergeist.

2

The Unnatural History of the Poltergeist

The term "poltergeist" implies that these psychic disturbances are caused by some type of "spirit" or demonic entity. As has been suggested by others, perhaps it would be better to use the term "poltergeistery," since we are really dealing with a *group* of diversified phenomena. These phenomena, as a whole, can be labeled "poltergeist disturbances" or "poltergeist-like disturbances." However, when a poltergeist erupts in a home it usually follows a rather standard pattern. During a typical outbreak, objects will suddenly move about or break by themselves. These antics usually last for only a few weeks or months, though. Generally the poltergeist centers on the family living in the victimized house and will follow them if they move to a new residence. Usually, but not always, the poltergeist will center on one specific family member. The PK may not even manifest itself unless that person is home or awake. Very often that agent is an adolescent around the age of puberty, or sometimes it is a mentally disturbed child or adult. While the poltergeist can cause considerable damage to property, only rarely does it actually hurt anyone— though this, too, has happened in a few instances.

And once a poltergeist burns itself out, it rarely recurs.

Many people tend to confuse poltergeists with "haunted houses," but there are several differences between these two phenomena. Unlike poltergeists, hauntings are usually long, drawn-out affairs that continue to activate over several years. A haunting is usually totally independent of its observers, and successive tenants might all witness the phenomena. In other words, hauntings infest a *place*, poltergeists infest a *person*. Rarely are objects hurled about by PK or crockery smashed during hauntings. Instead, one may hear footsteps, see apparitions, or confront other ghostly phenomena.

The range and diversified activities of the poltergeist are awesome. Although most cases follow a typical pattern, the actual manifestations of the poltergeist can be incredibly varied. No two cases are exactly alike. The following phenomena, though, are the most commonly reported:

Raps and blows. Loud percussive blows are often heard emanating from the walls of a poltergeist-infested home. Often the blows sound more like detonations than knocks. In many cases the raps are heralds of more active poltergeistery.

Movement of objects. These effects can be quite diversified. Objects are often flung across rooms or sometimes are moved along weird trajectories. For example, objects may make odd zigzag movements or may move in slow motion as if being carried. Sometimes objects will merely fall off shelves or slide across counter surfaces. Often bottles will explode.

Raps and flying debris are only the most basic activities of the poltergeist. The following are some of the more bizarre effects that have been recorded by poltergeist victims and investigators over the centuries:

Stone-throwing. Sometimes rocks will bombard or merely fall down on the roof of a home afflicted by a poltergeist. In most instances the stones will pelt the outside of the house; yet there have also been some cases recorded in which stones mysteriously appeared and were hurled about *inside* the house.

Teleportation. During some outbreaks of the poltergeist, household objects will disappear—even out of locked containers—and then reappear elsewhere in the house. They may subsequently turn up in unusual places, or suddenly drop from the ceiling. Sometimes objects disappear and are never recovered.

Apparitions. While not a common phenomenon, apparitions have been seen in a few cases.

Fire-lighting. The poltergeist may also ignite mysterious fires. In one case recorded in 1695, fires were lighted several times in one day. No normal cause was ever found for the blazes.

Biting. Sometimes the poltergeist force will actually "bite" members of the victimized family. Witnesses have reported that bite marks, lacerations, and wounds appeared on their bodies during the infestation.

Any explanation of the poltergeist must take into account all of these effects. Unfortunately many contemporary parapsychologists, in their attempts to demythologize the poltergeist by showing that these phenomena are not caused by demons or spirits, have underestimated its power. It can be a more malevolent guest than generally believed. As anyone who has ever confronted a poltergeist or who has interviewed its victims will tell you, the poltergeist is something that must be fought as well as investigated.

The poltergeist is as old as mankind, although it was not until the twentieth century that we began to possess any understanding of it. Before the 1960s, when parapsychologists first began to study the poltergeist scientifically, there were some 375 cases reported around the world throughout recorded history. As might be expected, the more industrialized countries reported the largest log of cases. England reported 127; France, 58; the United States, 56; and Germany, 29. A few cases have also been reported from Canada, India, Russia, Spain, Chile, and Greece, and from virtually every other civilized country in the world.

The fact that poltergeist displays are more often reported in Western and technologically advanced countries is a telling point. As the well-known psychical investigator Hereward Carrington pointed out in his book *Haunted People* (which he co-authored with Nandor Fodor):

...Were poltergeists merely due to trickery, on the one hand, and credulity and superstition on the other, we should assuredly expect them in greater number in relatively uncivilized countries, or at least in those in which the level of culture is not high. But an examination of the material shows precisely the reverse....

Even the first scholars of history noted the existence and mystery of the poltergeist. Jacob Grimm in his *Deutsche Mythologie* cited an old German case. He reported how a house was bombarded by stones while blows erupted from its walls. These incidents occurred in A.D. 355. We know of a case recorded by Jaffé in his *Bibliotheca Rerum Germanicarum*, which occurred around A.D. 760, in which fires ignited, objects disappeared mysteriously, and a baby was reportedly hurled into a fire. Many Catholic saints reported that demons molested them by throwing rocks or pounded on the walls of their cells or monasteries. By the Middle Ages reports of such unexplained phenomena increased.

There was little attempt to verify the poltergeist during these early years. The witnesses and family members were usually too terrified to explore the nature of the beast. The bewildered family more often than not just called in a local priest as quickly as possible to banish the "evil spirits" by continual and frequent exorcism. Since poltergeists are usually short-lived, in many instances these prayers and exorcisms seemed to work.

However, the Dark Ages soon ended and man's basic fear of the unknown softened during the Age of Reason. People no longer automatically believed in witches and goblins, so, when a poltergeist erupted, the onlookers usually tried to find out who was perpetrating the fraud. Instead of the clergy, law enforcement investigators were usually the first ones summoned.

A very rational poltergeist account recorded during this era was reported by Robert Boyle, one of the founders of the Royal Society in Great Britain, and a talented scientist who pioneered the study of gases. (Every chemistry student is familiar with Boyle's law.) He was also interested in religious issues and in 1642 or so he met a Huguenot minister named Francis Perrault, who had been a poltergeist victim. Perrault had written a chronology of the affair shortly after the events had transpired, while the incidents were still fresh in his mind. Boyle, decidedly impressed by the minister's sincerity and prowess as a reporter, had the narrative published in English.

When reading this account, though, one should keep in mind that most of our current evidence points to the fact that the poltergeist is a form of parapsychological phenomenon engendered by a human being, although the person is not usually aware of having unleashed it. Consequently poltergeists often reflect the cultural climate and beliefs of the day. In the seventeenth century the poltergeist was believed to be caused by demonic activity, so it usually manifested itself in that very form and acted very diabolically. The poltergeist will often act in such a way as to conform to the expectations and beliefs of the observers.

The first displays of the Perrault poltergeist were not witnessed by the minister personally, but by his wife and maid. Upon his return home after a five-day journey, his wife frantically told him that she had been awakened from sleep one night by something that drew her bed curtains so noisily and suddenly that it also woke her maid. No cause could be found to account for the incident, which only heralded more poltergeistery. The wife and maid were sharing a bedchamber the next night when both felt something pulling at their blankets. The maid tried to run from the bedeviled room, but the door couldn't be opened. Some force was holding it closed. Luckily a youth who was in the house rescued them and was able to open the door from the outside without any difficulty. The maid then ran into the kitchen where she found the family's pewterware strewn all over the floor. The disturbance intensified the following night.

Perrault's initial reaction to the story was one that anybody might have had. He dismissed the whole affair as a practical joke. But Perrault's initial skepticism did not bar him from becoming the butt of the poltergeistery himself. After carefully investigating the house before retiring for the night, he was to witness the strange goings-on personally.

> Scarce was I in my bed, [he wrote] but I heard a great noise from the kitchen, like the rolling of a billet thrown with great strength. I heard also a knocking against a partition of wainscot in the same kitchen, sometimes as with the point of the finger, sometimes as with the nails, sometimes as with the first, and then the blows did redouble. Many things also were thrown against the wainscot, as plates, trenchers and ladles, and a music was made with a brass cullender. . . .

Having heard the noises for himself, Perrault was still in no way convinced that the cause was anything supernatural. Sword in hand, he began to search the house for the instigator of the mischief, but found nothing. Another clamor broke out as soon as he retired again to bed. Once more the weary Perrault fruitlessly searched the house for an intruder. The next morning he reported his observations to the elders of his church and to a local notary. The elders thereupon decided to investigate the house themselves, but apparently did not witness anything unusual.

This hide-and-seek game is typical of the poltergeist: the presence of visitors will often immediately put an end to the activity, which will then resume as soon as they leave. Actually this form of "witness inhibition" often occurs during laboratory ESP experiments as well. Early pioneers in the field of ESP research, among them J. B. Rhine, noted that a gifted subject would temporarily lose his or her ability when a new observer was introduced into the experimental area, but would regain it when he or she became more accustomed to the on-looker. Unfortunately, this principle has made investigating the poltergeist by reliable scientists difficult.

Finally, after several visits during which the investigators witnessed nothing at all, the poltergeist broke its silence and the party heard human-like whistles and even a few gruffly spoken words, which seemingly emanated from thin air. Interestingly enough, the production of actual human voices is one of the rarest poltergeist effects. Usually these voices only croak out a few words, yet in the Perrault case they became more talkative over the ensuing days.

The Perrault poltergeist seemed particularly aggravated by the presence of the minister's maid and she actually became the focus of its antics. As Perrault records:

Once he [the poltergeist] snatched a brass candlestick out of the maid's grasp, leaving the candle lighted in her hand.

One afternoon a friend of mine, one M. Conain, a physician of Macôn, bestowed a visit upon me. As I was relating to him these strange passages [experiences] we went together to the chamber where the demon was most resident. There we found the feather-bed, blankets, sheets, and bolster laid all upon the floor. I called the maid to make the bed, which she did in our presence, but presently, we being walking in the same room, saw the bed undone and tumbled down on the floor, as it was before.

Even these early witnesses were aware that the poltergeist was often linked to a single individual in the stricken house, and many of Perrault's friends believed that the maid was somehow responsible for the demon's activities. The poor girl was, quite understandably, suspected of witchcraft. Perrault noted that if the maid challenged the poltergeist to carry out some specific action, the requested activities would often occur in a matter of moments. Nonetheless no one could stop the annoying invasion.

As the days went on, the Perrault poltergeist grew in intensity. Stones were flung at the house from morning until night, and even the notary was struck by one of them, although it fell harmlessly at his feet. He marked the rock and threw it into the backyard of the house, only to be pelted again by the *same* rock later on. He also noticed that the rock was hot to the touch. For some reason, however, the stone-throwing epidemic ended the disturbance for good.

Although the Perrault case included some rather odd happenings, such as the production of human voices, it did follow a typical sequence of events. In the beginning of the infestation, only isolated incidents were recorded. The first consistent effects were rappings. These incidents eventually erupted into full-scale object-throwing, which subsided shortly thereafter. So it seems that this poltergeist actually gained force during its occupation of the house. At first the power was incipient, managing to produce only a few effects. It then was able to generate more force before dissipating. As we shall see, all this is typical of how the poltergeist operates.

Because of the era in which Perrault lived, he and others could not understand what paranormal potentials lay within the human organism. Since anything supernormal fell under the jurisdiction of the church, people could only interpret the poltergeist in terms of current religious beliefs and dogma. Poltergeist cases were therefore invariably dismissed as being caused by the activities of demons. However, the clergy were by no means immune to poltergeist attacks. (Remember, Perrault was a minister.) Another plagued the Wesley family in Great Britain, which included a thirteen-year-old boy, John, who later founded the Methodist Church.

John Wesley's father, the Reverend Samuel Wesley, was the main witness to the poltergeist that attacked his rectory at Epworth, Lincolnshire, in December and January of 1716–17. Fortunately many members of the family wrote detailed descriptions of the events and we have their diaries and letters to which we can refer.* Mrs. Wesley and her maid were the first to realize that there was something unearthly about the puzzling phenomena that began to upset their household. She wrote to her son Samuel:

On the First of December our maid heard, at the door of the dining-room several dismal groans, like a person in extremis, at the point of death. We gave little heed to her relation, and endeavored to laugh her out of her fears. Some nights (two or three) after, several of the family heard a strange knocking in divers places, usually three or four knocks at a time, and then stayed a little. This continued every time for a fortnight, sometimes it was in the garret, but most commonly in the nursery, or green chamber. We all heard it but your father....

Mrs. Wesley did not report the incidents to her husband, fearing that the religiously oriented man would interpret the happenings as portents of his own death. She, in fact, believed this herself. However, the

---

* For example, many of these letters and documents are reprinted in Harry Price, *Poltergeist over England* (London: Country Life, 1945).

knockings became so prevalent that the elder Wesley finally heard them one night when a series of nine raps resounded at his own bedside. Gradually the knocks abated and the Wesleys heard what sounded like people noisily walking up and down the stairs. Sounds of bottles being smashed were also heard, and the Wesleys could find no normal explanation for these odd noises.

In order to check his own observations, Wesley invited Mr. Hoole, a rector who lived nearby, to join the household. He too heard the popping sounds. Wesley subsequently even tried to communicate with the entity (or spirit) that they all believed was causing the disturbances, but he was able to get only more groans and rappings in response. The raps continued for the entire month of December and eventually gave way to more astonishing phenomena. Hetty, one of the Wesleys' daughters, testified that she had witnessed much more than merely raps. As Emily, another daughter, recorded in her letters:

Our dog was fast asleep, and our only cat [was] in the other end of the house. No sooner was I got up stairs, and undressed for bed, but I heard a noise among many bottles that stand under the best stairs just like the throwing of a great stone among them, which had broken them all to pieces. This made me hasten to bed; but my sister Hetty, who sits always to wait on my father going to bed, was still sitting on the lowest step on the garret stairs, the door being shut at her back, when soon after there came down the stairs behind her, something like a man in a loose nightgown trailing after him, which made her fly rather than run to me in the nursery.

Both girls were extremely frightened by the PK-mediated noises, so the power of suggestion plus the emergence of an odd shadow could easily have caused them to imagine the phantom.

Soon, though, the family nicknamed the poltergeist "Jeffrey" as it took on a primitive sort of personality and intelligence of its own. For example, if someone stamped his foot at the entity, "it" would often rap in reply. If someone yelled at "Jeffrey," magnificent raps would shake the house in response. In this case, then, the poltergeist did not merely consist of a rash of unconnected bits of senseless PK, but showed a very definite primitive intelligence. (This is a theme I shall return to later.) Undoubtedly it is for this reason that poltergeistic phenomena were and continue to be attributed to spirits or demons.

Apparitions of grotesque animals were also seen in the Wesley house and were verified by several independent witnesses. Emily Wesley wrote to her brother that at first the creature looked somewhat like a badger. A servant chased the apparition, which to him seemed to resemble a rabbit.

Animal apparitions, while rarely mentioned in accounts of modern poltergeists, were commonly reported during the seventeenth and eighteenth centuries. Usually the apparitions were described as almost gargoylish in appearance, but at other times assumed the appearance of more terrestrial animals. These apparitions were also probably cultural artifacts. For instance, the Wesleys believed that their poltergeist activities were somehow due to witchcraft. Of course, everyone knew that witches were supposed to possess "familiars," supernatural beings that often took the form of small animals who carried out the sorcerer's evil bidding. Since this belief was commonly held in the early eighteenth century, it is not odd that the poltergeist (which was believed to be caused by witchcraft) should most accommodatingly produce apparitions in keeping with the cultural beliefs of the day. The English-Canadian poltergeist authority A. R. G. Owen has even suggested that many legends about Brownies and other tricky spirits may have developed from genuine poltergeist outbreaks.*

Eventually several of the clergy urged the Wesleys to move from the afflicted house, but the elder Wesley, who never flinched from his religious convictions, maintained that he never need fly from the devil. And after two months, the disturbances did come to an end.

The Wesley poltergeist was not a particularly forceful one. Poltergeists are often much more intense and violent. One case reported from this period, which illustrates just how vicious the poltergeist can be, has been called "the Bell Witch," since it also was thought to be the product of enchantment. In fact, this poltergeist culminated in a murder, although one can only surmise whether the poltergeist was responsible for the act or was merely used as a convenient cover-up for the crime.

The Bell Witch was a typical "family poltergeist," which plagued the home of John Bell, his wife, and their nine children, one of whom, Richard William Bell, kept a diary of the events. The Bell Witch is peculiar in that it lasted a great deal longer than most poltergeists do and

* See his article, "Brownie, Incubus, and the Poltergeist," which appears in the Autumn 1964 issue of the *International Journal of Parapsychology*.

later recurred. It first made its appearance in 1817 and lasted about four years. The poltergeist returned again in 1828. The persistence of the Bell Witch served as a prelude to its malevolence.

As with more conventional cases, the coming of the poltergeist was heralded by knockings and scrapings on the outside of the doors and windows of the house. Soon afterward the sounds moved inside. Witnesses heard and reported noises that sounded like dogs fighting, or like objects rolling over the floors. These ceased when the family members searched the house. The noises literally assaulted the home and finally focused on Elizabeth, one of the daughters, who was actively persecuted by the poltergeist. During the banging and crashing, one of the sons was awakened when he felt his hair pulled:

"Immediately Joel yelled out in great fright," he wrote, "and next Elizabeth was screaming in her room, and after that something was continually pulling at her hair after she returned to bed."

Realizing that they needed help, the Bells called for James Johnson, their neighbor. His presence did not cause the disturbances to abate, but the poltergeist finally retreated after he invoked the name of the Lord. However, it soon erupted again with new violence, again focusing on Elizabeth.

It was Johnson's belief that an intelligence was at work behind the incidents. So at his request several other friends were invited to the house to investigate the matter and ensure that none of the family members were responsible for the disrupting events. In the meantime Elizabeth made a quick retreat to a neighbor's home, but the poltergeist followed her. What was even more bizarre, though, was the fact that the Witch soon began erupting in open fields and in other houses near the Bell home.*

The Bell Witch employed an annoying repertoire of disturbances during its siege. Flickering lights would appear on the Bells' front yard, and the family and their servants were often struck by flying stones and pieces of wood as they walked about the grounds. Eventually, though, two øf the Bell boys were caught flinging sticks at passersby. (They were apparently imitating the effects occurring in their house.) It seems hard to believe, though, that the boys could have been faking *all* the phenomena attributed to the Bell Witch. But this case alerts us to a most interesting mixture of both genuine and fraudulent manifestations.

The Bell household frequently tried to get the Witch to speak. Whistles and faint whispers were heard, and these voices eventually became quite powerful. During this time twelve-year-old Elizabeth (or Betsy, as she is called in the reports) began to show signs of severe mental illness. She suffered from fainting spells, an inability to catch her breath, and often had to gasp for air. The onset of these symptoms seemed directly related to the times when the poltergeist was most active.†

* The cause of these symptoms may help to explain the Bell poltergeist. Elizabeth was probably suffering from hysteria, a neurosis engendered by intense subconscious guilt or trauma. The sufferer usually projects this guilt inwardly and punishes herself (it is much more common in women than in men) by developing pathological symptoms such as paralysis, the inability to swallow, continual faintness, etc. Could the Bell Witch have been a PK-projected form of Elizabeth's hysteria? This is a theme I shall return to later.

† It is common for the poltergeist to follow its primary victims, who, as I have pointed out before, are probably causing the disturbances to begin with. But on rare occasions a poltergeist will also infest neighboring houses. Few poltergeist investigators are aware of this

Not only did the poltergeist seem to become more powerful, it also seemed to grow in intelligence. It even began to whisper in a creaking voice, "I am a spirit who was once very happy, but has been disturbed, and made unhappy." John Bell soon became the butt of the persecution. He was struck severely by invisible hands and constantly molested. Mysterious voices threatened the entire family. In fact, many different voices were heard during the height of this unusual case. During these weeks there were prolific apport manifestations (materializations) as well. Objects would unexpectedly appear out of nowhere, apparently teleported into the room; and walnuts, grapes, and other odd objects would fall from the ceiling. Pins were found stuck in furniture and in the beds, and Betsy even began to vomit up pins and needles. Needless to say, no one could determine how they got there.

Other phenomena which plagued the Bells were yet more unpleasant. William Porter, a friend of the family, was asleep in the house one night when he was awakened by a force trying to pull off his bedclothes. He grabbed the covers and tried to throw them into the fire. He wrote:

In an instant I grabbed the roll of covers in my arms and started to the fire, intending to throw the covers, Witch and all, in the blaze. I discovered that it was very weighty and smelled awful. I had not got halfway across the room before the luggage got so heavy and became so offensive that I was compelled to drop it on the floor and rush out of doors for a breath of fresh

---

fact. Such events cannot be explained by the theory that the poltergeist-focus is himself producing the effects. They indicate that the poltergeist is a much more complex phenomenon than many parapsychologists would have us believe.

air. The odor emitted from the roll was the most offensive stench I ever smelled....

Upon returning to the room, he found the odor was gone.

During the next phase of the case, the poltergeist became even more malicious toward John Bell. He was beaten, hurled about, and finally poisoned by a potion mysteriously placed in his medicine bottle. (As I stated earlier, it is not known whether the poltergeist really committed the murder or was used as a cover-up for the crime—even though the voice of the Witch took credit for the deed.) After John Bell's death, the disturbances ebbed and then one night, as Richard Bell recorded, "Something like a cannon ball rolled down the chimney and out into the room, bursting like a smoke ball." The poltergeist was over.

The phenomena recurred seven years later but this time with much less force. It pulled covers from beds, knocked and rapped, erupted briefly in the home of another family member, but terminated after only two weeks.

No doubt there was much fraud perpetrated during the Bell Witch case, but we will never know exactly how much. However, many of the manifestations were witnessed by independent observers. More important, though, the case does counter the popularly held belief that the poltergeist is a harmless rackety ghost. The Bell Witch's maliciousness was horrifying and one can only wonder at the horrendous power and hatred that gave it birth.

Not all poltergeists are so forceful. Some, as typified by the Wesley case, are restricted to only a few minor effects. Others are still weaker. For example, a case almost contemporaneous to the Bell Witch was the Bealings Bells case of 1834, which illustrates not the grandeur of the poltergeist, but the poltergeist in its weakest and most puerile form.

The Bealings Bells case gets its peculiar title from the strange fact that mysterious bell-ringings were the only phenomena reported by Major Edward Moor, the chief witness to the incidents that plagued his poltergeist-ridden house in Great Bealings, Suffolk. The incidents began on February 2. Upon returning from church Moor was told by the servants that the household bells (activated by bellpulls) used to summon them had rung by themselves on several occasions. The ringings often emanated from unoccupied rooms. After hearing this bizarre tale, Moor examined the bell wires to see if anyone had tampered with them. While doing so, he and his son actually observed the bells ringing violently seemingly of their own accord. The ringing occurred again ten minutes later and subsequently all during the day. But they were only a prelude to what was to come.

The bells continued to ring for more than fifty days straight. They were oftentimes so violently rung that the din couldn't be imitated or produced in any normal way. Moor even tried forcefully pulling the bell cords himself with all his might, but the subsequent noise was meager compared to what the poltergeist could produce. Moor was no fool by any means, and didn't immediately jump to the conclusion that a ghost was loose in his house. He first considered the possibility that a servant or other human agent was causing the disturbances, so he carefully ascertained the positions of all members of the household whenever the ringings occurred. Each time, though, he had to conclude that no member of the household was responsible for the incidents.

After Moor published an account of his poltergeist, he began to collect other accounts of bell-ringing poltergeists. For example, an almost identical case was brought to his attention by a woman who had witnessed similar events in her own home. As she wrote to Moor:

...One afternoon in July 1835, the bell of one of the sitting rooms was observed to ring loudly several times; no person having touched it. In the course of half an hour the same thing occurred with nearly (if not) every bell in the house. Sometimes one would ring singly; then three or four together. The wires were distinctly seen to descend, as if pulled violently.

I sent for the bell-hanger; but before he arrived, the noise had ceased. He examined all the wires, without being able to discover any cause for this singular occurrence, and was about to take his leave, as it was growing dusk, when the bells again began to ring more violently than before. One we particularly noticed at this time, belonged to a room immediately over the passage in which the bells rang. It is pulled by drawing up a little slide against the wall; and the wire merely passes through the floor to the bell below. The slide we watched for more than five minutes. It was constantly shaken; even making a rattling, and the bell ringing.

The woman reported that the wires continued to shake even after the bells had been removed. She then went so far as to gather all the servants together to make sure that it was none of them shaking the bells. Totally dumbfounded, she ended her account on a note of consternation as to what had caused the incidents.

Up until the 1850s poltergeists had usually been explained in one of two ways. They were believed caused by either demons or fraud, since there was generally very little understanding of psychic phenomena during this era. Around the middle of the nineteenth century, though, scientists began to explore the nature of psychic phenomena in more depth and a new understanding of the poltergeist began to emerge at this time. In fact, this newborn scientific interest in psychic phenomena was partly due to a poltergeist that broke out in Hydesville, New York, in 1848.

In December 1847 Mr. John D. Fox, his wife, and their two daughters, Maggie (aged fourteen) and Kate (aged twelve) moved into a small two-story wooden cottage in Hydesville, a small town in New York State. A few months later they began to hear what sounded like knocks emanating from the walls. The two girls subsequently discovered that, if they rapped their fingers against the wall, the raps would be returned. This suggested to the Foxes that the entity plaguing their home was endowed with some sort of intelligence. Neighbors were soon called in to witness the strange proceedings. One of them, William Duesler, was able to communicate with the poltergeist by means of a primitive code. As the alphabet was recited, the poltergeist would designate letters by rapping at the appropriate moment. Another neighbor, Chauncy P. Losey, even quizzed the poltergeist about his personal affairs. He literally challenged it to answer personal questions such as reciting the ages of his children. He ended his written deposition on the Hydesville rappings by reporting, "I think that no human being could have answered all the questions that were answered by this rapping."

The force behind the poltergeist probably gained this

information by telepathically tapping the questioner's own mind. As I said earlier, an intelligence which can employ PK, such as a human mind, can usually also employ ESP.

Mrs. Fox and the girls were too frightened to stay in the house that first night, so only Mr. Fox and a neighbor stayed behind. But the news of the "haunting" soon leaked out and large crowds flocked to the cabin in order to observe what were to become known as the "Rochester Rappings." By this time, by means of a code, Fox had actually procured a "story" from the poltergeist. The spirit of a traveling salesman claimed to be causing the ruckus and asserted that he had been murdered in the cottage.*

The raps continued for several days and centered on the two children. Of course, the naïve townsfolk of the 1840s knew nothing about PK or how it could emanate from a living mind. Instead, they assumed that the phenomena were caused by spirits of the dead. This belief soon became the basis for a new religion, Spiritualism, which spread like an epidemic throughout the United States. This new creed taught that man could contact the dead through psychics, and that the dead could manifest themselves to the living through apparitions, poltergeists, and the like.

* The truth or fiction of the "ghost's" account is a matter of debate. E. E. Lewis, a local publisher who checked into the story, uncovered some evidence that previous tenants of the house had also reported peculiar phenomena there (which would lead to the conclusion that the Fox cottage was haunted and was not the focus of a true poltergeist), and one witness even claimed to have knowledge of the murder. But there was little hard evidence to support the tale. There were also reports that human remains were found when the cellar was excavated, but this report was never truly documented.

The subsequent story of the Fox sisters is a rather grim one. They became professional mediums, giving séances and producing raps on demand, and soon newspaper reporters and scientific organizations sent committees to test them. Some certified that their abilities were genuine, others condemned them as frauds. Even the great English chemist Sir William Crookes tested Kate Fox and was impressed by the raps she produced. Later in their careers the girls were the victims of mob violence, succumbed to alcoholism, and finally confessed to fraud only to retract their confessions later. Today it is impossible to determine how much ability the Fox sisters really possessed.

The charges of alcoholism and fraud that blemished the Foxes' careers do not offset the fact that many unbiased witnesses heard the raps that began disturbing the house in March 1848. However, the Fox case is historically important to our understanding of the poltergeist for several reasons: (1) the case prompted the first scientific studies of psychic phenomena in the United States; (2) also for the first time, people came to believe that poltergeists were caused by spirits of the dead rather than by demons; (3) the scientific study of the poltergeist commenced at this time. All three of these factors subsequently led to the scientific development of parapsychology (or psychical research).

The science of parapsychology was born, so to speak, in 1882 when concerned British Spiritualists and Cambridge University intellectuals decided to form an organization whose primary function would be to rigorously and skeptically evaluate reports of people with psychic abilities and to investigate spontaneous occurrences of ESP, PK, apparitions, and hauntings.

They hoped that their organization could sift the genuine reports from the morass of self-delusion and outright fraud that was tainting the Spiritualist movement as well as all phases of the occult. This new society, subsequently named the Society for Psychical Research (SPR), was more critical and hardnosed than the founder-Spiritualists had expected, and many of them dropped out. This left a core of scholars who were extremely skeptical of the very existence of many forms of psychic phenomena, such as the poltergeist. Instead they focused their attention on people with telepathic and clairvoyant abilities and mediums who claimed to receive information from the dead.

The first parapsychologists learned quickly that investigating the poltergeist was no easy matter. It came as little surprise to them that most people are not very accurate when describing events from memory. Furthermore the SPR investigators discovered that most people are not very good observers at all. As more and more poltergeist cases were studied they discovered that if three different people witnessed the same incident they often reported very different versions of it. (Anyone who has sat in court and listened to two or three different versions of the same traffic accident can testify to that.) This led some poltergeist investigators to suspect that many PK reports were merely the result of poor observation. Often the witness's accounts did not specifically note where the household children were located when objects were being thrown about. Could the children have caused the disturbances, they wondered? If two witnesses told two different versions of the same story, who was to be believed? Eventually, these first psychical researchers tended to discount poltergeist reports unless competent investigators—such as themselves—could see the incidents firsthand.

This attitude caused certain difficulties, though. As I pointed out earlier, poltergeists do tend to go into hiding when new observers are introduced on the scene. Unaware of this effect, many nineteenth-century psychical researchers visited poltergeist-ridden residences, observed nothing, and concluded that the families had not been bold enough to fake anything while they were present. As soon as they left, though, the nuisances often recurred. The poltergeist soon gained a bad reputation among psychic researchers, and many investigators seriously began to wonder if there really were such a thing as a genuine poltergeist. After all, fraud was usually suspected and frequently uncovered during many of the cases the SPR investigated during these years. (Even as late as 1938 W. H. Salter, an official of the Society for Psychical Research, wrote in his *Ghosts and Apparitions* that he questioned whether there was any such thing as a genuine poltergeist.)

Nonetheless a few of the early investigators were able to witness the poltergeist's eerie displays at firsthand. One notable case was reported by Sir William Barrett, a noted Dublin physicist and a founder of the SPR. Barrett had investigated a poltergeist in 1877, five years prior to the founding of the society. The family consisted of a widower who lived in Derrygonnelly with his five children, aged ten to twenty. As with most poltergeists, this one focused on a single individual—the farmer's twenty-year-old daughter Maggie.

Raps were this poltergeist's forte, and when they resumed on the evening of Barrett's visit, he sent a co-investigator to patrol the outside of the house to be sure no trickster was involved. Meanwhile, accompanied by the widower and his only son, Barrett approached the room in which Maggie and her three sisters slept. Although three of the girls were asleep, Maggie was awake and was lying in clear view on the bed with her hands and feet uncovered. Barrett illuminated the room with a lamp and although this appeared to inhibit the raps at first, they gradually started thumping again, resounding from the walls and ceiling of the bedroom. As the physicist reported, "The closest scrutiny failed to detect any movement on the part of those present that could account for the noises, which were accompanied by a scratching or tearing sound."

The rappings gave way to more peculiar events. As Barrett's narrative continues, "Suddenly a large pebble fell in my presence on to the bed; no one had moved to dislodge it even if it had been placed for the purpose."

The Derrygonnelly poltergeist could purportedly rap out answers to questions verbally or telepathically addressed to it. Barrett was perhaps the first trained investigator to probe this phenomenon personally. As he reported:

I mentally asked it, no word being spoken, to knock a certain number of times, and it did so. To avoid any error or delusion on my part, I put my hands in the side pockets of my overcoat and asked it to knock the number of fingers I had open. It correctly did so. Then with a different number of fingers open each time, the experiment was repeated four times in succession and four times I obtained absolutely the correct number of raps.

Toward the end of the nineteenth century pioneering psychical researchers in other parts of the world also began reporting their own personal encounters with the poltergeist. One case, which occurred in 1900 at an inn in Turin, Italy, was investigated by Cesare Lombroso (often credited as the founder of the science of modern criminology), who witnessed the PK when he was alone in the infested house. The disturbances took place in the inn's wine cellar where inexplicable breakage had been reported by the perplexed innkeeper, who also complained that his wine bottles often moved by themselves, and would sometimes break or explode for no apparent reason. Tables and chairs and kitchen utensils also flew around the room, he claimed. Fortunately Lombroso was not too late to observe the telekinesis (a term meaning "movement at a distance") himself under excellent conditions. As he recorded:

There was a deep wine cellar, access to which was obtained by means of a long stairway and a passageway. The people informed me that they noticed that whenever anyone entered the cellar the bottles began to be broken. I entered at first in the dark, and, sure enough, I heard the breaking of glasses, and the rolling of bottles under my feet. I thereupon lit up the place. The bottles were massed together upon five shelves, one over the other. In the middle of the room was a rude table. I had six lighted candles placed upon this, on the supposition that the spiritualist phenomena would cease in bright light. On the contrary, I saw three empty bottles, which stood upright on the floor, spin along as if twirled by a finger and break to pieces near the table. To avoid a possible trick I carefully examined by the light of a large candle, and touched with my hand all the full bottles standing on the shelves and ascertained that there were no wires or strings that might explain the movements. After a few minutes two bottles, then four, and later others on the second and third shelves separated themselves from the rest and fell to the floor without any violent motion, but rather as if they had been lifted down by someone: and after the descent, rather than fall, six burst upon the wet floor (already drenched with wine) and two remained intact. A quarter of an hour afterwards three others from the last compartment fell and were broken on the floor. Then I turned to leave the cellar. As I was on the point of going out, I heard the breaking of another on the floor. When the door was shut, all again became quiet.

Like many early investigators, Lombroso knew that a poltergeist is usually linked to a human agent. He naturally suspected someone at the inn. A young employee seemed to be the focus of the disturbances, and the poltergeistery ceased when he was dismissed.

Continental parapsychologists were, in fact, more interested in PK phenomena than were their English and American contemporaries, probably because they had had more opportunity to study people who could voluntarily exhibit PK. Therefore a further advance in our understanding of the poltergeist came at about this time. Some parapsychologists began to realize that poltergeists may have nothing at all to do with spirits of the dead, but be the psychic product of the human mind. (Previous investigators had realized that a connection existed between the poltergeist and its victim. But they had never ascertained just *what* this connection was.) However, other psychical investigators of this era, such as Camille Flammarion, believed that poltergeists could be caused by the powers of the living *or* the dead.

Nonetheless, few investigators during these years spent much time trying to solve the mystery of the poltergeist. They were more interested in observing the PK than trying to find an explanation for it. In this respect the first critical attempt to evaluate a large number of poltergeist cases was carried out by Frank Podmore, one of the early SPR coordinators, in 1896. His paper, entitled simply "Poltergeists" and published in the *Proceedings of the Society for Psychical Research*, is classic nineteenth-century parapsychological thinking about the poltergeist.

Podmore was extremely skeptical of poltergeist reports and changed his evaluation of them many times throughout his career. Sometimes he would be favorably impressed by a case, but other times he would remain resolutely skeptical about the very existence of the poltergeist. In general he felt that few cases showed any evidence of being genuine. Fraud was discovered in several; in others the observers disagreed; and in still others Podmore felt that the low educational level of the witnesses precluded them from giving reliable accounts. However, he was reluctant to dismiss one case, which he dubbed the Worksop Poltergeist, which had been primarily witnessed by Joe White of Worksop, Nottinghamshire.

The first manifestations observed by White and his family were mild. As they told Podmore, the PK began suddenly one day when the kitchen table lifted by itself, and displaced several objects on top of it. Two of his young children, as well as another child named Eliza Rose, who was the daughter of a retarded woman, were present in the house at the time. Several days after the table incident, Eliza and Mrs. White were alone in the kitchen when various objects including hot coals suddenly took flight, and over the next several days more items were thrown through the air. One incident so unnerved them that they began to scream. White stated in his deposition to the SPR that he rushed to see what had happened and upon entering the room was himself struck by a flying candle. Immediately after, a china figurine fell off the mantlepiece. White put it back, but it catapulted across the room immediately afterward. Since he had already summoned a few friends and neighbors to his house for moral support, there were several witnesses to these events.

Podmore concluded his report on the Worksop cases by saying that "With regard to the positions of the persons present, in relation to the objects moved, it may be stated generally that there was no possibility in most cases of the objects having been thrown by hand." Later, though, he became less sure about the authenticity of the case.

Despite his skepticism, Podmore made one extremely important observation about the poltergeist. In each case reported to him, a prepubescent or teen-age child was present in the infested home, and more often than not this child was a girl.

Over the years, other psychical investigators have documented this pattern more fully. Even contemporary parapsychologists have discovered that a family attacked by a poltergeist usually includes at least one adolescent. This pattern is so common that it is reasonable to assume that the poltergeist syndrome is inherently related to these children. In Podmore's day it seemed that female poltergeist agents far outnumbered the males. But this is no longer the case today. Over the last two decades more boys than girls have been reported as poltergeist foci.

Podmore's observation was certainly correct, but his interpretation was not. He failed to see that there existed a *psychic* relationship between these adolescents and the poltergeist. Instead he concluded that these children had merely faked the disturbances. He based this conclusion on the premise that fraud had actually been uncovered in many of the cases he had investigated. But here, too, Podmore's logic was probably very naïve. During the early years of organized parapsychology, researchers took an either/or approach to people who claimed psychic ability—either they were genuine or they were not. These investigators did not realize that poltergeists—as well as psychics—are often a mixture of both. Even in genuine cases children may seek to imitate the poltergeist, or use it as a cover-up for mischief. It is not at all unlikely that many of the bogus poltergeist cases the SPR investigators uncovered initially were genuine and were only later characterized by fraudulent activity when the children, enjoying the notoriety or attention they received because of the poltergeist, sought to prolong it.

A case I investigated along with my colleague Raymond Bayless (author of *The Enigma of the Poltergeist*) will illustrate the problems researchers may confront while trying to authenticate poltergeist manifestations.

Our investigation took place in 1974 after a gentleman from Inglewood, California (whom we'll call Mr. Holms here), called us to report that his brother's home was the scene of some typical poltergeistery. A few days before, he told us, the family had heard poundings on the walls of the house. These knocks sounded to them as if they came from *outside* the house. However, small objects began to fly around his niece's room soon after. These outbreaks usually took place in the evening after 9:30 P.M., we were assured, and lasted into the early morning hours. Mr. Holms also told us that, when he had first visited his brother's house, he had been struck by several small beads that had bombarded him from the kitchen. This was where his niece was standing, but he didn't think she had thrown them. He also claimed to have seen objects falling from the ceiling.

Things had apparently become intolerable the next day, and the family had called in law-enforcement officers, hoping that they could solve the mystery. Three officers visited the house but, again according to Mr. Holms, objects continued to move about the place even when all the family members were being watched. The family was so distraught by this time that they moved to a motel for the night. They had no idea that the poltergeist would follow them. And it was at this point that Raymond and I were called into the case.

It was hard to evaluate the case from the testimony. It was certainly possible that Holms's niece was projecting the PK, since she always seemed to be present when the disturbances broke out. In fact, according to the Holmses, objects were usually flying specifically from wherever in the house she was sitting or standing. So it was also possible that she might be counterfeiting the entire affair. Our first duty was, of course, to locate the police officers who had witnessed the events and get their statements, since their report might be more straightforward and objective than the family's. Raymond took over this responsibility and the sergeant on duty verified that, indeed, there had been a "family disturbance" at the Holms house the day before. He also verified that officers had been sent to the scene and even gave Raymond the case file number. Later on, though, I had cause to call the police about the case, but the officer in charge now began *denying* that any such case had been reported. It seemed that a cover-up was taking place and this made us even more curious about the case. So that night, accompanied by Mr. Holms, we began our personal investigation into the case.

Nothing happened in the first hour of our vigil, but as soon as we turned out the lights at the family's suggestion, a shower curtain hook flew across the room. Each time the lights were put out more objects were thrown from a table behind Holms's niece. Her fraud was obvious, and her little game was exposed when, in the dark, I propped my foot against her chair and followed it as she tipped it back to grab for the objects behind her. Raymond also caught on instantly and even intercepted her nimble hand as it reached for the objects. We tried to keep our observations to ourselves, since the family was convinced that a real poltergeist was at work. However, it soon became clear to us that the observations reported by the family were absolutely worthless. For instance, an ashtray was thrown across the room during our stay and the family all claimed that this object was kept on a table totally out of their daughter's reach. This, however, was not true, since I had previously made a diagram of where all movable objects in the house were located. This diagram clearly showed that the ashtray in question was kept on the table where the girl was sitting when it was thrown.

By this time Mr. Holms himself caught on to his niece's machinations. But she adamantly denied any wrongdoing when he directly accused her of fraud. Obviously a family storm was brewing so Raymond and I, thanking the family for their hospitality, consoled them by advising them that—*whatever* the nature of their phenomenon—it would soon abate. Then we left.

It is impossible to say what degree of authenticity was present in this case. The initial raps, followed by conventional object-throwing, all fell neatly into the pattern of a typical poltergeist. Yet all we saw was trickery. I would have preferred to continue our investigation that night to see if anything evidential might have taken place, but the mood of the family made it unwise for us to stay. It was unfortunate, though, that the sheriff's office did not let us interview them. They were the only ones who could have shed some light on the mystery.

It is no wonder that the first poltergeist hunters became disillusioned when cases similar to this one were so often uncovered. And we can sympathize with Podmore, who interpreted the presence of children in so many poltergeist cases as an indelible indication of fakery. Indeed there *was* a relationship, but not the one he believed existed.

By the turn of the century it was well known that the poltergeist was linked to a human agent. But a few researchers still wondered if these individuals were perhaps only contributing energy to a spirit or demon who was actually perpetrating the poltergeist. However, this belief was permanently discredited in 1905 when a case was reported from Sweden that clearly demonstrated a relationship between our innate PK potential and the poltergeist. A rural villa was the scene of the outbreak.

The main observers of these events were Hjalmar Wijk and Dr. Paul Bjerre, two investigators who stayed at the villa shortly after violent rappings were heard in the home of a forestry inspector and his young wife. It didn't take the investigators long to discover that the raps occurred only when the inspector's wife, Karin, was present.

Karin was twenty-seven at the time. During the last few years, she had been under a severe emotional strain. She was melancholy, according to her husband, and suffered from depression, fainting fits and tremors, anxiety attacks, and paroxysms. (These are all symptoms of hysteria.) The attacks had gradually become less frequent and had tapered off considerably by the time the raps commenced. However, Karin had had confrontations with the paranormal before the poltergeist eruption. Three years before, she had toyed with "glass psychography" (a form of Ouija-board writing) and had become adept at it, although nothing very impressive was ever received through the writing. However, a personality named Piscator spelled out his name and soon became Karin's regular guide. She had, however, given up the writing long before the appearance of the poltergeist.

Poltergeist phenomena usually begin when the unfortunate family is alone, but this case was different. When the poundings first started, several of the inspector's associates were visiting. Karin was just on the verge of falling asleep one night when she awoke with a start to the sounds of footsteps parading on the veranda outside her room. These were accompanied by loud knocking noises. A normal explanation for these sounds was soon found, though. One of the house guests had been marching around outside trying to find his way about the villa in the dark and had knocked on a door that he had found locked! Karin returned to bed somewhat relieved, only to hear the same wooden knocks as before.

They continued all night long. She dismissed the whole affair as a practical joke, never realizing that the subsequent raps were heralding the onset of the poltergeist. Her attitude changed dramatically the next day when she, her husband, and a maid heard thunderous poundings from the villa walls. A diligent search failed to uncover any natural cause for the disturbances. The raps seemed to stay close to Karin and followed her from room to room, while quiet reigned only when she left the villa altogether.

Karin and her husband left the house on several occasions, and the perplexed couple gradually began to see a pattern in the poltergeist manifestations. When Karin was away from the house no raps were heard, either in the villa or at the house where she was staying. But the raps would become as frequent as ever as soon as she returned home. If she became unduly upset, the raps activated accordingly. On rarer occasions, they would also start upon her direct request or command.

In light of the odd events plaguing them, Karin and her husband decided that, in order to get to the root of the problem, they might do well to consult Piscator, Karin's former guide, through her glass-rolling. (The glass is used like a pointer on a Ouija-board. The alphabet letters are spread out in an arc on a table.) Piscator, of course, manifested promptly and claimed responsibility for the raps.

Wijk and Bjerre first visited the couple and investigated the raps only after the occurrences had tapered off, but they soon realized in talking with the couple that the rappings were associated with Karin's subconscious. For instance, they learned that the raps often occurred just as she was about to fall asleep and that she would have inexplicable anxiety attacks before an outbreak. In order to alleviate these attacks, Bjerre began hypnotizing Karin and it was through the use of hypnosis that the experimenters first began to understand the poltergeist. By questioning the entrance agent and Piscator through her, the investigators were actually able to explore the nature of the raps. Bjerre even suggested to the soi-disant "spirit" that he should produce raps that very night at 11:00 P.M. The hypnotic session was an outstanding success, for the raps started their furious pounding, after several days of silence, at the appointed hour that night. But while it was clear that the raps could be manipulated by hypnotic suggestion, Karin was thrown into convulsions by the poundings.

Bjerre and Wijk knew they were on to something by this time, so during the next few days they frequently hypnotized Karin and gave her instruction to produce the raps at appointed hours. The sessions were usually successful and the investigators were able to make detailed observations about the raps, since they knew when to expect them. In fact the PK even accelerated during this period of the case.

The hypnosis had a peculiar effect on the raps, though. At first they invariably broke out in response to the hypnotic suggestions, but then gradually lapsed back into their former unpredictable outbursts. Even Karin's unconscious mind began noticeably to resist any hypnotic suggestions given it, though the girl herself began to develop an increasing desire to undergo the hypnosis. Finally the investigators told the hypnotized Karin that Piscator—whom they "blamed" for the poltergeist— would leave, never to return, hoping that this suggestion would end the rappings once and for all. However, this suggestion had a reverse effect, and the raps began to break out spontaneously and uncontrollably. In hopes of understanding the reason behind this unexpected delay, the investigators hypnotized Karin the next day:

"Why were there rappings yesterday afternoon?" asked Bjerre during the session.
"Because I was so nervous," Karin responded.
"Wasn't it Piscator who came?"
"No, it was only because I was nervous."

This brief dialogue was extremely enlightening, for it revealed that on a subconscious level Karin was aware that she was producing the raps. Until this point in the case, Piscator really existed in her mind. It was now clear, though, that he had indeed followed the hypnotist's suggestion, had "gone," and had merged back into Karin's subconscious. The raps soon ceased, but later sporadically recurred. Since Wijk and Bjerre did not follow up the case after issuing their 1905 report, we don't know Karin's (or the poltergeist's) ultimate fate.

Bjerre and Wijk were probably the first investigators ever to explore the psychological dynamics underlying the poltergeist. Although Karin was not the usual "disturbed adolescent" with whom we normally associate the poltergeist, she had the typical personality of the usual poltergeist victim. The raps had a definite meaning for the frustrated, nervous, and hysterical Karin: they relieved pent-up anxiety and acted as a safety valve for her own inner conflicts.

The Karin case illustrates that the poltergeist is just as much a psychological mystery as a psychic one. Even in 1905, when the study of psychology was still in its infancy, experts were beginning to realize that the poltergeist was an outgrowth of the mind's inability to cope with strain and was not due to the surreptitious activity of supernatural entities.

This theory was further confirmed during the next step in science's effort to understand the poltergeist when investigators began trying to bring the poltergeist into the scientific laboratory. This, too, is a fascinating story in itself.

The first laboratory-investigated poltergeist case on record was originally reported from Romania, where an adolescent girl named Eleanore Zugun was the center of consistent object-throwings and window-breakings in the 1920s. Her superstitious parents were terrified and believed that demons were causing the disturbances, but the local priest could do nothing to exorcise the phenomena. In fact, when a local patron saint was invoked in the Zugun home by the townsfolk in an effort to stop the poltergeist, a stone mysteriously flew through the room and smashed a picture of the saint hanging on the wall. Her parents had no alternative but to dispatch Eleanore, around whom the events focused, to various friends in their hometown of Tulpa. But the villagers were just as confused by the PK as the girl's parents had been, so beat and threatened the girl with incarceration in an insane asylum unless the telekinesis stopped. Finally the villagers decided that the only thing they could do was send Eleanore to a convent, but the poltergeist followed her even there, and reports of the strange case soon appeared in the presses throughout Europe.

At about this time, Fritz Grunewald, a German parapsychologist, decided to look into the case and learned that Eleanore had in fact been sent to an insane asylum. Through his cajoling, though, Eleanore's father had her released and returned to the convent where Grunewald carefully observed and took care of her. For several weeks he personally witnessed many of her incredible PK displays, and soon realized that it was impossible to allow Eleanore to stay with the harsh and superstitious villagers. He thereupon made arrangements for her to go to a private home in Berlin where he could continue his scientific investigation of her PK. Unfortunately Grunewald died from a sudden heart attack while making these critical arrangements and Eleanore was left in even more unfortunate circumstances than before.

Countess Zoe Wassilko-Sereki, a Romanian patroness of psychic studies living in Vienna, came to Eleanore's rescue at this time. In 1925 she managed to adopt the girl and brought the case to the attention of some of the best German parapsychologists of the day. However, the breakthrough in the Zugun case came when the English poltergeist expert, Harry Price, made a quick trip to Vienna to witness the still active poltergeist for himself. He wrote:

I found Eleanore to be an intelligent, well-developed, bright girl with a sunny disposition. She was nearly thirteen years old. The Countess and I seated ourselves on the couch and watched Eleanore playing with a toy that fascinated her: a spring gun that projected a celluloid ping-pong ball, which was caught in a sort of conical wire basket that was attached to the gun. Suddenly, as we watched, the ball came to pieces, its component halves falling at our feet. The girl ran to the Countess and asked her to mend it. She jumped up, and so did I. As I watched my hostess examining the join, a steel stiletto with handle, used for opening letters, the whole about ten inches long, shot across the room from *behind* me and fell against the closed door. I instantly turned round and a minute investigation revealed nothing—and no one—that could have projected the stiletto, which was normally kept on the writing table behind us, against the wall farthest from where we stood....

But these were not the only PK effects Price observed during this trip. As he goes on to report:

...a large black cloth dog that Eleanore used to cuddle, shot from the study side of the room, over the partition, and fell on to the coal-scuttle near the bed. No one was nearer the dog... than ten feet, and Eleanore, at the moment of the flight, was pushing a table against a wall using both her hands. Then I saw a cushion on one of the chairs begin to move. As I watched, it slid *slowly* off the chair and fell to the floor. No one was near it....

In order to investigate Eleanore more fully, Price invited the girl and the countess to his own National Laboratory of Psychical Research in London, which was probably the best-equipped laboratory of its kind in Europe. During the first days of her visit, witnesses watched small objects fall from the ceiling of the laboratory and strike the girl. (Eleanore attributed these pranks primarily to *Dracu* [devil], a being she felt was harassing her.) These displays were also observed by Price, and on one occasion he discovered that one of Eleanore's apports (see page 53) was an enameled metal notice-board letter of the type used on the building's bulletin board. On checking, Price and his astonished colleagues discovered that the letter had been psychically removed from a box that had arrived only the day before. Furthermore, the letter box had been kept in a closed cupboard and in a room four stories below. Only a very few people even knew that the box had arrived. Yet the very letter that had fallen on top of Eleanore was missing from the box.

These apports and other PK displays were observed under stringent conditions. However, Price's attention was soon called to an even more bizarre manifestation: biting and scratch marks began to appear on Eleanore's body. As Price reported, Eleanore would often suddenly shout out in pain as she played, and ugly-looking welts, red scratches, or actual teeth marks would immediately rise on her arms, face, or chest. The teeth marks were identical to her own, but they were often inflicted in places not accessible to her own bite.

The raising of these bite and welt marks were even filmed by Price and his co-workers. Copies of the film are still in existence. Eleanore is seen sitting before a small table while the experimenters are standing about her. On the table is a drawing of *Dracu*. Eleanore is given a hammer by one experimenter and is urged to strike at the picture. (Eleanore believed that *Dracu* would bite her if she offended him.) After a few good bludgeons, a close-up shot shows horrid-looking welts raising on her body. It is fascinating footage.

At face value there might not have been anything paranormal about the bites. In fact very similar markings can be produced on volunteer subjects by the use of hypnotic suggestion. The marks do, however, indicate that Eleanore had an unconscious tendency toward self-abuse, of which the poltergeist was probably a psychic projection. But sometimes these self-attacks were augmented by more provocative telekinetic displays. At times, when Eleanore cried out, pins and needles were found mysteriously jabbed into her flesh.

Price had the insight to bring the case to the attention of several psychologists who, in turn, gradually discovered the unconscious meaning of the stigmata. It seems that Romanian villagers often menace children with the threat that the devil, or *Dracu*, will "get them" if they are naughty, just as children of previous decades in American culture were threatened with the "bogeyman." *Dracu* was associated with biting and scratching. So when the poltergeist broke loose, Price's colleagues believed, Eleanore naturally associated the disturbances with the devil and all the horrid things with which he supposedly tormented children. Unconsciously she was torturing herself with the fantasies that had been instilled in her as a very young child.

Even after Eleanore left London, and after Price had witnessed her PK manifestations in his own laboratory, the case remained active. The last incident he recorded was perhaps puerile, but a fitting climax to her visit. During her stay at the National Laboratory, small objects and letters from the bulletin board often fell from the ceiling or mysteriously appeared in the room with Eleanore. To rule out the possibility of fraud, Price had the box containing the enamel letters locked and hidden away. Despite this precaution, some of the letters still disappeared, including one of the "C" letters. One day Dr. R. J. Tillyard, an Australian etymologist and a collaborator in some of the tests, dropped in to bid the countess and Eleanore goodbye before they all returned to their respective countries. The farewell was cordial but Tillyard was brief and never came closer than an arm's length to the Viennese visitors. Later that day, when aboard a commuter train, Tillyard reached under his overcoat and into his jacket pocket for his penknife, and found the letter "C" inexplicably placed there. Earlier in the day he had checked through his pockets but had found nothing. The "C," on the other hand, had been lost for eleven days.

Upon their return to Austria, the countess and Eleanore were victims of a rather vicious newspaper attack, which accused them both of fraud. The countess decided to sue and a long, drawn-out court proceeding resulted. But in the end the judge ruled that the newspaper attack was justifiable criticism, and the countess lost the case.

The poltergeist attacks came to an abrupt end at about this time, and Eleanore lost her powers just as her first menstruation began.

This odd parallel in the Zugun case between the beginnings of sexual maturity and the cessation of the poltergeistic PK is probably more than mere coincidence. Since the poltergeist is often born from psychological conflicts, could sexual conflicts also play a role in some cases? Could the poltergeist be allied to sexual frustrations or energies? The presence of puberty-aged children in so many cases strongly suggests this possibility. There even seems to be some direct evidence that the onset of adolescence—with all the psychological tensions and difficulties that accompany it—might be a time when the poltergeist is most likely to erupt.

Uncovering sexual traumas and conflicts deep within the subconscious has always been the job of the psychoanalyst, as he probes the history, emotions, and goals of a patient. As is well known, Freud discovered that much of our behavior is an unconscious reaction, often symbolic, to our preoccupation with sex. It should not seem surprising, therefore, that the rapid development of psychoanalysis during the 1930s offered the next insights into the nature of the poltergeist as a few psychologically oriented investigators began to realize that sexual conflicts might be at the heart of at least some cases.

The search to find a sexual base for the poltergeist, which was only suggested by the Zugun case, began in earnest in 1938 when the London-based *Sunday Pictorial* carried the headlines GHOST WRECKS HOME, FAMILY TERRORISED, along with a story about a house in Thornton Heath (a suburb of London) that was the scene of violent PK activity including flying crockery, eggs, pans, and coal. News reporters had visited the house and seen the manifestations themselves. They had even witnessed Mrs. Forbes, the lady of the house, being wounded by a piece of china that catapulted through the air and gashed her arm. The *Daily Mirror* soon picked up the story and gave it added publicity when one of their reporters described how an eggcup exploded right in his own hand.

Psychical investigators arrived to investigate the outbreak only five days after the onset of the disturbances. Usually families are so reticent about reporting poltergeists that by the time the parapsychologist arrives the principal events have waned. All the investigator can do then is interview the witnesses and hope that some minor PK events will take place in his presence. This wasn't at all true in the Forbes case. Quick to the call was Dr. Nandor Fodor, a Hungarian lay-psychoanalyst. Fodor was also an avid student of the paranormal, and after coming to England had become the director of the International Institute for Psychical Research (IIPR). The institute was run by Spiritualists, but its work was not spiritualistically oriented and it explored many aspects of psychic phenomena. Fodor in fact was definitely not a Spiritualist, but had been entrusted with directing research and investigating cases which came to the institute's notice.

Fodor's arrival on the scene did not inhibit the poltergeist at all. In fact the psychoanalyst remained at the house all day and witnessed some twenty-nine incidents, although most of them occurred when Mrs. Forbes was not watched and she therefore could have faked the occurrences herself. Fodor's notes are impressive, though. The following is an extract from his book on his investigations, *On the Trail of the Poltergeist:*

1:50 P.M.   Mrs. F. coming from kitchen with plate in both hands. I see her from sofa clearly over threshold. *Ping!* In kitchen tumbler on floor near back door, unbroken. *Evidential.*

1:52 P.M.   Mrs. F. comes from kitchen with pudding plate, very nervous, holding it with both hands, is in full view. *Ping!* Same glass in kitchen off table, unbroken. *Evidential.*

1:55 P.M.   Mrs. F. comes from kitchen hugging saucer and three cups to her breast with both hands. She is in full view. *Ping!* The same saucer off kitchen table, unbroken. *Evidential.* Spoons are needed, Mrs. F. dared not go out. David [her son] fetches them. Nothing happens.

2:15 P.M.   Mrs. F. sits on hearthstone with cup and saucer in hand. *Ping!* I see cup flashing by. Misses Mr. F.'s head by fraction of an inch. Cup a yard away unbroken. Saucer, falling straight down, smashes on hearthstone. *Impressive.*

And when Fodor brought Mrs. Forbes to his

laboratory at the IIPR, the poltergeist followed. No sooner had she stepped into the offices than a brush was noisily thrown from behind her. Later other small items (usually belonging to Mrs. Forbes and presumably brought from her home) were flung about intermittently. Fodor, though, was in no way sure that Mrs. Forbes was not throwing the objects herself when no one was looking, but he conducted some experiments with her nonetheless, and during the rest of the day items were continually thrown about. Objects were even flung inside the car in which she and Fodor drove; while other items mysteriously disappeared from rooms in which they were sitting, only to reappear spontaneously later on just as strangely. All in all, the total range of poltergeist effects witnessed during the case included the movement of objects, the smashing of china, raps, the disappearance of objects, apports, and odd odors. Later, though, Fodor was able to prove that Mrs. Forbes had faked at least some of the PK.

The main importance of the Thornton Heath poltergeist investigation rests with the psychoanalytic studies Fodor used to unravel gradually the underlying trauma that had prompted the PK outbreak in the first place. During her interviews with Fodor, Mrs. Forbes described certain previous experiences, which alerted him to the possibility that a hidden sexual conflict existed in her mind. Years before the onset of the poltergeist disturbances, Mrs. Forbes reported to Fodor, she had fallen into an unexpected sleep in which she dreamed that her father was forcibly pulling her toward him. Toward the end of the dream he drew a red cross over her breast. The mark of the cross was still present when she awoke, and she was sent to a local hospital, where a columnar-celled carcinoma was found and removed from her breast. There was further evidence of sexual antagonisms between Mrs. Forbes and her father. She had married young, against her father's wishes, and even though he had forgiven her she suffered hysterical attacks during her married life. She had also suffered from periods of total blindness and once attacked her husband with a knife. It was clear to Fodor that her family was still a villain in her eyes; they disapproved of her collaboration with him, and had only given in because the poltergeist activated with renewed fury when they objected to his experiments. Fodor therefore felt that the poltergeist was actually a "bundle of projected repressions," and with that phrase he initiated a whole new concept of the poltergeist.

By exploring Mrs. Forbes's earliest recollections, Fodor uncovered a childhood fantasy that had continually manifested itself in her dreams. In this fantasy she was looking for the grave of a man who had done something ghastly to her when she was five years old. She did not know what this "something" was, but she wanted to see the man buried in a coffin. Ultimately Fodor traced this obsession to a presumed sexual assault on her by her own father, the anger over which she was projecting onto her husband with an almost murderous vengeance. Fodor logically deduced that the poltergeist was a projection of this same deep-seated unconscious hatred. It would have been fascinating to see if the memory of the attack could have cured Mrs. Forbes and ended the poltergeist (remember, Fodor's conjectures were based solely on inferential evidence from Mrs. Forbes's fantasies), but she never did recall the assault directly. Unfortunately this final denouement never came. Also, Fodor's investigation was being carried out under the auspices of the IIPR, whose spiritualistically inclined officers were becoming increasingly uncomfortable with his research as it gradually pinned the disturbance to a sexual cause. Sex was still a taboo subject, and the staid directors of the institute began putting more pressure on Fodor to change the avenue of his investigations. This he refused to do. A clash with his own governors was inevitable, and Fodor had to give up the investigation and part ways with the IIPR.

Were Fodor's observations correct, or were they merely the fantasies of a psychoanalyst? Many critics of psychoanalysis have argued that a therapist will often project his own biases into what his patient is reporting. Furthermore, fantasy and reality are often confused in the subconscious mind. Even Freud himself was initially aghast when he uncovered evidence that many of his female patients had been raped by their fathers, until he realized that these recalls were probably only fantasies and did not represent actual occurrences. Could Fodor have found a fictitious sexual basis for the poltergeist because he was looking for it?

These are questions that have no simple answers. But Fodor's classification of the poltergeist as a "bundle of projected repressions" is one of the most important insights in the history of poltergeist research. He, more than any other investigator before him, realized that the poltergeist was a vehicle of expression, that it was actually a projection of hostility and repression. With this in mind, let us summarize the psychodynamics of the poltergeist, especially when children are the cause.

During a typical poltergeist, the events will center around one person in the victimized family. In all the cases cited in this chapter, the presence of a particular "poltergeist agent" was either discovered or implied. This is the first clue to understanding these PK demonstrations. All of us have our angers and frustrations, which we resolve in a variety of ways. The most simple is by direct display of our emotions: I get angry, throw my pen across the room, and I feel better. Or I can yell at someone who has annoyed me. There are other ways I can vent my hostilities. I can "act out" my aggression by defacing property, or "displace" my aggression by yelling at my secretary after being scolded by my boss. To be more passive, I can "deny" my anger by convincing myself I have none at all. By doing this I am not resolving any conflict, I am merely "repressing" it. Sometimes I might depend on a "reaction-formation" that is, develop a trait exactly opposite to my secret feelings. For example, a miser who hoards money may be reacting to his real tendency to spend recklessly. Or I can even "project" my hostility by convincing myself that everyone *else* has the anger or tendencies I fear in myself. These methods of handling conflicts are not abnormal; we all use them to some degree, and they are part and parcel of our normal use of defense mechanisms.

What has all this to do with the poltergeist? The poltergeist appears to be the psychic manifestation of some of these same defenses. Many poltergeist victims (for example, Mrs. Forbes and Karin) seem to be actively repressing psychological or sexual hostilities from consciousness, or psychologically denying them altogether. These feelings still exist subconsciously, however— for some people it is easier to deny or repress emotions than it is to acknowledge them. Could Mrs. Forbes have handled the knowledge that she secretly hated her father? It is doubtful. Children often are unable to express frustration or anger without reprisal from their parents, especially since their hostilities are usually directed *toward* their parents.

I'm sure that all parents have seen how their child will run to his room when scolded and slam his door noisily; rip up pictures of adults out of magazines; or write all over the walls. This is normal behavior for a child. He is displacing and acting out his frustrations, since he cannot directly strike back at his parents—emotionally binding figures—who have punished him. But when too much anxiety-provoking feelings and emotion are repressed into the subconscious, something is bound to give and this can lead to neurotic behavior.

When frustrations are so repressed and denied from consciousness that the victim cannot express them normally, the hapless individual may use PK—albeit unconsciously—to carry out the very acts he would consciously like to do but is inhibited from executing. At the simplest level, this is what causes the poltergeist. The poltergeist throws things, pounds on walls, breaks things, and annoys people in the household. These are all things that a child or immature person does quite normally when frustrated. But, for some as yet inexplicable reason, some people—especially children— are able to employ their psychic potential to carry out these acts for them. As a matter of fact, many poltergeist investigators have noted how "childish" the poltergeist acts.

This is, of course, a rather simple explanation for the poltergeist, though many parapsychologists have even come to believe that this model can explain the entire nature of the poltergeist. I, however, cannot totally agree with this position. While this psychological milieu is obviously the breeding ground for the poltergeist, it does not seem to be the total explanation for the phenomena. The usual poltergeist *does* admittedly follow this pattern, which has become part of a rather predictable "poltergeist syndrome." But these may only be the mildest forms of poltergeist outbreaks. Other more complex poltergeists might be due to more complex causes and dynamics. Poltergeists often show intelligence and even a will of their own. Some of their activities cannot be accounted for psychologically. I believe that stone-throwing, fire-lighting, apportations, and the like shed a different light on the poltergeist. Those who believe that the poltergeist is *merely* the projections of a frustrated adolescent are severely underestimating the poltergeist and its powers. It may be that there are different types of poltergeists, which we classify together merely because they share common characteristics.

3

The Rampaging Mind

Years ago one would only have been able to share in the astonishment at the puzzling events brought on by a poltergeist. But now our infant understanding of the poltergeist enables us not only to witness it, but actually to help the family through it. Although poltergeist investigators have been vaguely aware of the etiology of PK for some time, it has been only within recent years, as many modern cases have been probed and evaluated, that the psychological nature and setting of the typical adolescent poltergeist has been more fully confirmed. This was the setting that Nandor Fodor and others had merely conjectured. How this pattern was substantiated is due to a great extent to the work of two parapsychologists working independently and in different countries.

Very close to one of the Duke University campuses in Durham, North Carolina, are two frame houses. These inconspicuous buildings house the Psychical Research Foundation, a nonprofit parapsychology division founded in the 1960s for the specific purpose of exploring those psychic phenomena that suggest that the human mind might survive death. The foundation's archives also house what is perhaps the world's richest collection of information on the poltergeist. William G. Roll, Danish by birth, English and American by education, and an active poltergeist hunter by occupation, is the project director for the organization. Roll has probably had more firsthand experience with the poltergeist than any other living parapsychologist and his research has added significantly to our knowledge of this form of PK.

In Germany, where parapsychology is more integrated with general psychology, Dr. Hans Bender, a psychologist with professional degrees in many other fields as well, has long headed the Institute for the Study of Border Areas of Psychology and Psychohygiene at Freiburg University. Like Roll, Bender has also witnessed the poltergeist and has helped to mold the "new view" we now have of the phenomenon.

These two investigators have been able to verify and analyze several modern poltergeist cases, and in this chapter their work, as well as the story behind their search, will be discussed.

The poltergeist has never been a terribly popular creature among parapsychologists. Parapsychology left the cops-and-robbers type of on-the-spot investigations around 1930 and moved into the laboratory when ESP testing became especially popular. Also at that time, scientific contributions made by the oldfashioned psychical research societies waned as college psychology departments all over the United States began to take over the task of researching ESP. And, as parapsychology became more entrenched in the laboratory, researchers lost much of their interest in people who claimed to possess the ability to levitate tables and perform other telekinetic displays. Parapsychology was concerned with proving the existence of ESP to the exclusion of all other areas of study. It did not take long, though, before even these researchers began to obtain evidence in their laboratories that the mind could directly influence matter. For example, J. B. Rhine, while working at Duke University, discovered that some of his subjects could influence the fall of dice by making them land on specific sides or in particular combinations more often than chance could account for. Soon everybody was throwing dice. Dice bias was checked for, statistics analyzed and reanalyzed, but the investigators always reached the same conclusion: by an act of will, the human mind could influence physical matter. PK research soon became something of a fad and experiments showed that the mind could influence falling drops of water, metal balls and cubes, spinning coins, and other objects as well.

The "new" and scientifically documented evidence for the existence of PK gave old tales of rampaging ghosts a little more credibility...but not much. You see, every new generation feels that it and only it is objective and careful in its work, and that previous reports and observations, dusty with time, are somehow suspect. So in spite of the excellent testimony from firsthand witnesses such as William Barrett and Harry Price, parapsychologists felt that they had to prove the reality of the poltergeist all over again. A few cases were scientifically investigated in the 1930s–1950s, but these cases were usually ignored by most experimental parapsychologists. It was this renewed interest in observing and exploring the poltergeist, however, which eventually led to the discovery of the basically unconscious factors at the root of the usual adolescent poltergeist. Modern interest in the poltergeist was sparked by two cases, one reported from New York and the other from Scotland. These two cases ultimately led W. G. Roll to pursue the poltergeist as almost a full-time occupation.

The case that opened new pathways in the study of the poltergeist occurred in Seaford, Long Island, where prolonged poltergeistery plagued the James Herrmann family in 1958. As with many family poltergeists, the first outsiders to watch the PK antics were the police. In fact Detective Joseph Tozzi, of the local police division, became one of the chief sources of information about the Seaford poltergeist. In February 1958 he followed up on a complaint from the family about some bizarre events that were taking place in their home. They claimed that small objects were falling from shelves, flying about the house by themselves, or mysteriously overturning. Bottles seemed to unscrew and even "pop" their caps off. All of these events had been observed by the Herrmanns and their two children, Lucille (aged thirteen), and Jimmy (aged twelve). Patrolman J. Hughes, who was also on duty that night, had originally answered the call and, when all the family were present with him, he heard sounds of the disturbance coming from a bathroom. No tremors or high-frequency equipment could be detected that could have caused any of the difficulties the Herrmanns were reporting.

As with so many poltergeists, the Seaford disturbances came to the attention of parapsychologists only after local papers started to publicize the case. When J. B. Rhine, who was then still director of the Duke Parapsychology Laboratory, read about the case, he quickly dispatched two associates, Dr. J. Gaither Pratt and W. G. Roll, who had just come from England to work

under Rhine, to investigate it. After initially interview-
ing Officer Hughes, Pratt and Roll were able to
substantiate that *something* unusual was going on at the
Herrmann house. The police officer testified to the
investigators that a bottle had actually fallen by itself
while he had been at the house. Unfortunately he had not
personally witnessed the event. Mr. Herrmann, however, seemed to be a good witness and his calm testimony
about the proceedings was a great asset to the
investigation. His testimony about the odd events
plaguing his house was full of precise detail:

He testified, for instance, about one detail:

At *about* 10:30 A.M. I was standing in the doorway of the
bathroom. All of a sudden two bottles which had been placed on
the top of the vanity table were seen to move. One moved
straight ahead, slowly, while the second spun to the right for a
45 degree angle. The first one fell into the sink. The second one
crashed to the floor. Both bottles moved at the same time.

The Herrmanns had recorded over sixty PK incidents
by the time Pratt and Roll arrived. Judging by typical
poltergeist standards, then, this outbreak—characterized
by thumping noises and the displacement or flinging of
objects—was fairly mild. However, certain fragile
objects had become "favorites" of the poltergeist and
were continually disturbed until they were finally broken.
One figurine was moved four times and finally smashed
into a secretary ten feet away.

One of the most prolific effects noted during the
Seaford disturbances were bottle "poppings," i.e.,
popping sounds that accompanied either the movement
of a bottle or the unscrewing of its cap. All together,

twenty-three bottle incidents were recorded among the sixty-eight events the Herrmanns reported.

With these facts in mind, Roll and Pratt spent several days at the Herrmann home, hoping to witness the PK. Their vigil eventually paid off. One evening both investigators heard a loud "thud" emanate from the cellar, and found that a bottle of bleach had fallen against the side of a cardboard box left near the washing machine. In addition the bottle cap was loose. The incident suggested that a poltergeist was active in the Herrmann home, but it was not convincing proof. Unfortunately the poltergeist seemed on the ebb by this time and Roll and Pratt were never able to see any of the alleged PK taking place.

As their investigation proceeded, the police as well as the investigators conducted painstaking research as they attempted to find a normal explanation for the events plaguing the Herrmanns. First Roll tried to determine if any chemicals placed in screw-cap bottles could cause the loosening of the bottle tops; but he was unable to find any substance that would cause such a reaction. The police hypothesized that high-frequency radio waves might be responsible for producing tremors that might cause stationary objects to fall over, but an oscillograph placed in the cellar failed to record any such activity. Wires, fuses, and everything else electrical in the house were thoroughly checked, nor were there any underground water sources that could have caused tremors in the house. (The movement of underground streams is a popular theory used by skeptics to "explain away" the poltergeist.)

The only consistent fact the investigators found when they analyzed the PK events was that they usually occurred when young Jimmy was up and about, and abated when he was away from the house or asleep. This, of course, suggested that the boy was either normally or paranormally responsible for the PK. Detective Tozzi had at one time even tried to get a confession from Jimmy, but the boy refused to admit to any wrongdoing. Actually, on many occasions all the family members were accounted for when the disturbances occurred, so it was unlikely that fraud alone could explain the case. But the events, meager to begin with, petered out during the investigation, so Roll and Pratt soon left...both intrigued and disappointed.

The case for the poltergeist was given added impetus in 1960 when reports of a mild but active case in Scotland was reported in the press. This poltergeist was persecuting eleven-year-old Virginia Campbell and her relatives in the small town of Sauchie and had been witnessed by a minister, three physicians, and Virginia's school teacher.

To understand the Campbell case, though, one must first understand the background events that apparently led up to its eruption. These factors shed important light on the psychology of the poltergeist.

Virginia was a rather lonely girl. She had been raised in Ireland where her closest companion was her pet dog, Toby. Mr. Campbell, however, wanted to settle in England and Virginia was consequently shunted off to stay with her brother and his wife and family in Sauchie while her father's various business transactions were completed. Virginia was shy, withdrawn, of normal intelligence, big for her age, and was going through the onset of puberty at the time.

The first indications that a poltergeist was loose in the

Campbell home came when raps and unexplained thumps began emanating from the walls of their house.

The bumping noises heralded even more active PK. The very next day Virginia's brother and his wife saw a sideboard creep a few inches away from the wall and then back again. That night loud banging erupted in Virginia's room and one witness, the Reverend Mr. Lund, discovered that the noises were coming from the headboard of the girl's bed. He could even feel their vibrations when he placed his hand on the bed. Moments later the startled minister watched as a seventeen-by-fourteen-inch fully loaded linen basket levitated, floated over an eighteen-inch path, and then moved back to its original position.

A few days later the poltergeist followed Virginia to school. Miss Steward, Virginia's teacher, later told investigators that soon after the onset of the poltergeist she observed the girl trying to hold down the top of her desk in the schoolroom. It appeared to be trying to open by itself. To her utter amazement she also saw an unoccupied desk situated behind Virginia rise about one inch off the floor and then settle back down.

At about this same time Virginia started to be plagued by psychological problems herself. She started talking in her sleep, calling out for a playmate she had left behind in Ireland, and for her dog, Toby. The sleeping girl was given a teddy bear to placate her, but this patronizing overture raised her ire and she flung it away violently, crying hysterically.

In the meantime, the British Broadcasting Corporation (BBC) had become so intrigued by reports about the Sauchie case that they sent a crew to Scotland to tape and record the phenomena. They eventually succeeded in recording some of the PK-mediated noises. Only sporadic PK occurred over the next few weeks, and it eventually died down, ending the affair.

Because of the number of independent witnesses to the case, the Sauchie poltergeist was a particularly evidential one. Like the Seaford case, though, it was certainly not a particularly violent one. Nevertheless, the range of PK effects observed during the case and in full light was impressive.

One of the chief investigators of the Sauchie case was A. R. G. Owen, a Cambridge geneticist who has given a comprehensive analysis of the case in his book *Can We Explain the Poltergeist?* He believes that the instigating causes of the poltergeist were Virginia's rapidly evolving pubescence, the emotional trauma instigated by her move to Scotland, and her general unhappiness.

I personally believe, however, that we can take Owen's suggestion a little further. Virginia was not only unhappy, but also very hostile, yet unable to express the anger she must have felt over being separated from her old home and friends. Since her parents were away she had no emotionally binding figures to "strike out" at. Virginia may have also unconsciously viewed her relatives as co-conspirators in her unhappiness. Therefore the poltergeist may have represented a form of defiance against the parents and brother. But, as Owen states in his report, "Virginia's case is indeed replete with suggestive possibilities. Firm conclusions cannot of course be drawn...."

Today contemporary psychology has developed splendid psychometric testing methods for uncovering conflicts and unconscious hostility. Some of these tests are merely questionnaires or attitude surveys, but they can reveal a good deal about an individual. Other tests (e.g., the Rorschach ink-blot test) are more subjective.

For example, in the Thematic Apperception Test (TAT), the subject is asked to make up a story about a cartoon-like scene he is shown. (The subject will tend to reveal his own conflicts by projecting them onto the scene he is interpreting. A skillful psychologist can, by interpreting the subject's responses, learn a great deal about the way the patient views himself and others.) If Virginia had been counseled by a trained psychologist, or taken computer-analyzable personality tests, what would we have learned about her and, correspondingly, her poltergeist?

These are the types of questions that W. G. Roll, working in the United States, and Hans Bender, in Germany, were pondering at the time that the Sauchie case became public knowledge, and they have been trying to answer them ever since.

Roll had another opportunity to explore the poltergeist at firsthand in 1967 when Susy Smith, a popular writer on the occult, informed him that she had received news of some poltergeist activity erupting in a Miami warehouse. Just as with the Seaford disturbances, the police had been called in to investigate when Alvin Laubheim, the owner of the business, reported that a ghost was loose on his premises. The police are not especially fond of receiving this type of call, but they began to take the report more seriously when one of their own officers reported that he had seen a glass fall from a shelf by itself and smash on the floor. Laubheim and a nineteen-year-old Cuban refugee employee named Julio were at the warehouse when the officer first arrived. Over the next two hours more police arrived and patrolled the storeroom, but failed to find any prankster hiding in the warehouse. The notions and souvenir items that were stocked on the warehouse shelves kept right on falling to the floor, breaking noisily. Since the warehouse had row upon row of tall multi-tiered shelves, rarely did the witnesses actually see the objects topple. Instead they would *hear* crashing noises emanating from unoccupied areas of the building and, upon investigating, would find mysterious breakage strewn around the floor. It was as though a ghost really were loose in Miami. Laubheim subsequently admitted to the police that there had been a disproportionate amount of breakage during the previous months, but he had thought that carelessness among the shipping clerks was the cause. But now, he admitted cautiously, he was beginning to realize that a more bizarre force was at work.

When news of a poltergeist breaks, reporters are quick to the scene. Susy Smith was in Florida at the time publicizing over the radio a forthcoming book on ghosts when a listener called in about the Miami poltergeist. Never willing to overlook a good story, the author investigated the report herself the next day. Since W. G. Roll was an expert on the poltergeist, she tried to call him in Durham, but he was away on business. Ms. Smith finally reached him in Louisiana, and after she filled him in on the details, Roll hopped the next plane to Miami.

By the time he arrived, Ms. Smith had already made detailed notes about the objects that had been disturbed and the trajectories of their flights. She had even seen a plastic tray fly from one shelf to another, and had once succeeded in goading the poltergeist into action. She reported:

... everyone went out for lunch except Julio and me. Someone had brought me food and I was eating at the desk. Julio was standing beside me at the south end of the room and no one else was in the room at twelve noon. I said to him, "This would be a good time for something to happen." At almost that instant the sound of a shot glass landing on the cement floor was heard. I have heard this almost enough to identify the sound by now. We found it inside the.roped area between Tiers 2 and 3 . . . it was not broken.

Roll must have thought that if there ever were an active poltergeist to be captured by a trained investigator, this was it. But the poltergeist seemed to go into hiding on the very day of his investigation. While a Coke bottle broke by itself in the storeroom soon after his arrival, the next day's vigil was nearly fruitless even though a beer mug toppled from its shelf as he was leaving the building. Roll began to realize that the poltergeist was playing cat and mouse with him. If he left the premises, the poltergeist would strike only to retreat the moment he returned.

Luckily some of the poltergeistery took place the next day in Roll's presence, convincing the investigator that the case was still active and required investigating. Unfortunately Roll had to be getting back to Durham. He returned to Miami shortly after, though, accompanied by J. G. Pratt, an associate and a well-known parapsychologist.

Roll now hoped to study and evaluate the Miami poltergeist by placing carefully chosen items (which he called target objects) in strategic locations throughout the warehouse. His plan was to rigorously watch these targets, thus assuring himself that no strings were attached to them if they should move. The plan paid off, as the following incident indicates.

An alligator-shaped ashtray was chosen as one of

these target objects. It was subsequently placed on one of the tiers close to where Ms. Smith was stationed. This was located in a section of the room where the poltergeist had been particularly active during previous PK outbreaks. Julio placed a cowbell, which the poltergeist had moved on several occasions, in front of it. After the objects had been set in position, the waiting began. Quiet reigned as everyone waited for the poltergeist to make its appearance. Then suddenly an argument broke out between Julio and a visitor to the stockroom. Roll was observing them both.

I was looking at Julio [reports Roll in his book *The Poltergeist*,] who was just about to reply to Miss Rambisz when the alligator ashtray crashed to the floor behind him. The cowbell remained in place, so the ashtray either must have moved over or around it. I could discover no way in which Julio or anyone else could have produced this event normally. I had Julio and the others under observation and examined the target area myself. No one had been near it since my last examination.

The Miami poltergeist continued to act up for a few days and never changed strategies. Each day it toppled small objects from the storeroom shelves. But Pratt and Roll used each object movement as a datum for later analysis: Where did it fall? From what shelf? What distance did it traverse? Where was everybody located at that precise moment? Having all these data at hand, Roll used the Miami information to determine if any discernible pattern seemed to govern the PK.

But what about Julio? By now it was evident that the handsome, dark-complexioned nineteen-year-old was the activator of the disturbances and that the poltergeist would manifest only in his presence. Soon Roll and his colleagues began to focus more on Julio than on the PK and they became the first modern investigators to make a thorough examination of the personality of a poltergeist agent. They went far beyond the type of psychoanalytical conjecturing that Fodor had attempted. But, like Fodor and Harry Price before him, Roll's plan was to try to harness the poltergeist right in the laboratory, so he invited Julio to Durham, where he could be tested at the Foundation for Research on the Nature of Man (FRNM).

Julio did not perform well on standard dice-throwing PK tests, but there were a few surprises in store for everyone during his stay at FRNM. One of the machines used for testing PK (a cage used to throw the dice) kept malfunctioning when Julio was working with it. Perhaps this too was due to Julio's innate PK powers. But apparently even the poltergeist itself had followed Julio to Durham. Roll writes in his report on the case:

At 9:35 we were taking a break in one of the offices. Julio was standing in the doorway to the hall with a cup in his hand when we suddenly heard a crash. When we went out to look, we found a large decorative vase or bottle which had been on the table on the other side of the hallway in pieces on the floor. The base of the bottle and the glass stopper were intact but the neck had broken into about 50 pieces. The area of impact being five feet or so from the bottle's position on the table. It had been about 16 feet from Julio and had moved toward him.

This incident occurred only an hour after Roll and Julio had arrived at FRNM and Julio was still being kept under strict surveillance.

There were two other witnesses to the vase incident, one of whom was Charles Honorton, who later took over direction of the Maimonides Medical Center's parapsychology division. I questioned him about the incident during a trip I made to New York in 1975. He told me something that sparked my interest. As he explained, the vase did not sound as if it broke when it fell, but at the critical moment he heard what sounded like an explosive pop. Honorton should have heard breaking glass, but heard a boom instead. He had been standing very close to Julio at the time and was sure that the teen-ager could not have maneuvered the vase by trickery.

Honorton's report intrigues me because many poltergeist witnesses have described how conventional object-throwings are sometimes accompanied by detonation-like pops. Sometimes these witnesses have also heard more conventional sounds, such as glass breaking or furniture moving about in unoccupied rooms, only to find everything in order upon rushing in there. For example:

- Raymond Bayless once recounted to me that, while holding vigil in a haunted house, he heard what sounded like every dish in the kitchen being broken to bits. He rushed into the kitchen, but found everything in order.

- In my previous book, *In Search of the Unknown*, I reported on a poltergeist which rampaged in a Van Nuys, California, apartment. Mrs. Ceccato, the primary witness, told me she once heard thunderous noises emanating from the kitchen. They could be heard, though, only when she stood in that room. As soon as she stepped into the hallway, there was absolute silence. But she could hear the sledgehammer-like blows as soon as she stepped back into the kitchen.

• Bottles were often heard to smash during the Wesley poltergeist, but none was actually broken.

These noises do not seem to be caused by any objects actually being thrown or broken. They represent a unique phenomenon in their own right. They represent a rather unappreciated aspect of the poltergeist.

Julio was a psychologist's delight. As soon as he arrived in Durham, both parapsychologists and psychologists began questioning and observing him to see if they could isolate any unusual personality traits that might throw new light on the poltergeist. Julio did not appear *severely* disturbed, and had functioned normally during the course of his job and during the investigation. Yet two psychologists evaluated him and they both came to similar conclusions.

The first evaluation was made by Gertrude Schmeidler, who is herself a psychologist, a parapsychologist, and a specialist on personality testing. She evaluated Julio's responses to various psychological tests and uncovered the pertinent facts that he had been brought up to appreciate high moral standards but harbored feelings of rejection, guilt, and unworthiness. Utter passivity was a basic component of his personality, and so he had difficulty expressing his feelings of unhappiness and aggression.

Another psychologist, Dr. Randall Harper, was just as firm in his conclusions. He stated that Julio harbored "aggressive feelings which are disturbing and unacceptable to him." He also found that Julio tended to divert any overt display of these feelings, and in fact shrank from assertiveness of any sort.

Julio was basically a typical poltergeist agent. He was hostile, but subconsciously preferred to deny his feelings rather than risk expressing them. It is therefore no wonder that he let loose a poltergeist from the depths of his unconscious mind. The PK could strike out in a way that he could or would not do normally. Although he was nineteen, rather older than most typical poltergeist agents, Julio had projected the poltergeist to disrupt his boss's business. He was obviously seeking to strike out at an authority figure, and his employer had become his psychic scapegoat. Roll and his associates also found that Julio had been having severe problems at home with his stepmother immediately before the onset of the poltergeist. He had also been suffering from nightmares. (Nightmares are themselves subconscious reactions to guilt.) Finally, he had been compelled to leave home. Julio even seemed bent on self-destruction, and he eventually began committing petty crimes, such as theft, for which he knew he would be caught and punished. In fact it was clear to the Durham psychologists that Julio *wanted* to be caught. (After the poltergeist abated, Julio continued having conflicts with the law and ended up in jail on several occasions.) His psychological turmoil obviously projected itself inwardly as well as outwardly (via the poltergeist). It often seems, in fact, as though the poltergeist most actively persecutes the very person who gives it birth. Eleanore Zugun even used PK to stick pins in herself. Julio took another path by engaging in sociopathic acts for which he knew he was bound to be caught and punished.

Julio is not the only poltergeist agent upon whom we have clinical data. Roll had made similar evaluations of other poltergeist agents before (and after) the Miami case that corroborated much of what he learned from Julio. For example, Roll had been summoned to Newark,

New Jersey, in 1961 when a poltergeist began playing havoc in the home of an elderly black woman and her thirteen-year-old grandson, Arnold. Roll brought them to Durham to see if the poltergeist could be observed in the laboratory. The case seemed to be genuine, but the boy began to fake poltergeist-like displays while he was in Durham. This episode signaled to Roll that the poltergeist had probably ebbed permanently. However, the trip enabled psychologists to examine Arnold and they learned that he had suffered an extremely traumatic childhood. He had been raised by several different foster parents because his real father had beaten him and his mother was more often in jail than out. She had once even tried to kill her husband. Predictably Arnold used denial to handle the conflicts tormenting him. In fact one psychologist who interviewed him stated in his evaluation:

> Throughout the three interviews the most striking feature was the degree to which he used denial and repression as defenses. There was considerable evidence of an intense, underlying anger towards his grandmother, but he was never able to verbalize this.... when it was gently suggested that he must feel quite annoyed at his grandmother at times, this was immediately denied, and he would attempt to change the subject.

> Another psychologist who was able to evaluate Arnold had the same diagnosis.

> Looking first at Arnold's personality, the most striking feature emerging from this examination is his massive use of repression and denial.

Roll is not the only poltergeist investigator who has uncovered these recurring psychological patterns. A report of a poltergeist summoned Dr. John Palmer, a psychologist from the University of Virginia's Division of Parasychology, to the rural southern town of Powhatan (a fictitious name used in the report) in 1968, where a ten-and-a-half-year-old black boy was living with his foster parents. (It is interesting to note that a great number of poltergeist agents are children who are living away from their natural parents.) The victimized family first became aware of a poltergeist when stomping noises began emanating from their basement. However, it was almost a month before full-scale PK became evident. Dr. Palmer brought the boy to the University of Virginia for psychological and neurological testing. The evaluating psychologist in this case, Mrs. W. S. Langman, knew nothing about the nature of the poltergeist. (The psychologists Roll had consulted during his investigations had been aware that they were dealing with poltergeist victims and were quite familiar with the "poltergeist syndrome." It could therefore be argued that Roll's evaluators were projecting onto their subjects the very traits that they *expected* to find. The psychologist in the Powhatan case did not know why she had been summoned, so her opinions and assessments may well have been more objective.) Nonetheless Mrs. Langman independently concluded that her young patient—though he didn't realize it—was suffering from many psychological debilitations which seem common among poltergeist victims.

"His general approach to life situations is passive and submissive—in coping with feelings of aggression, he tends to deny, to avoid, and to withdraw. In general, he pictures himself as unwanted and feelings of rejection are experienced," she concluded. One of Mrs. Langman's most interesting comments was that, when the boy's normal defenses are threatened, he was likely to act in an "unpredictable and irresponsible manner." And what could be more unpredictable than the poltergeist?

Despite the rich number of observations he was able to make on the Miami case, Roll still had very limited experience in actually observing the poltergeist in action until a major case broke out in Olive Hill, Kentucky, in 1968. During that investigation he personally saw a table levitate, rotate in the air, and fall back on the chairs surrounding it. It could possibly have been the most active poltergeist Roll was ever to investigate, but the family was extremely superstitious and uncooperative. The poltergeist was the devil's work, they declared, and Roll and his fellow parapsychologists were the demon's helpers. Consequently Roll and his associate had to leave after making only a few direct observations at the infested house.

Aside from merely investigating several cases, Roll has also tried to make some sense out of the poltergeist and its wild displays. He has, for example, devoted much labor to learning about the mechanical principles that seem to govern the poltergeist. He has charted the trajectories of poltergeist-thrown objects, analyzed the physical constitution of these objects, and has carried out extensive analyses into the scientific meaning of these data. In consequence, Roll believes that the poltergeist is actually governed by certain semiconsistent laws and restrictions.

Fundamental laws govern how physical objects move

when a force acts upon them. If you throw a baseball, for instance, there is a predictable way to judge how far the ball will travel before it will lose its thrust and fall to the ground. This is known as the inverse square law, for the object loses thrust according to the inverse square of the distance. If, however, a baseball is thrown through a denser medium than air such as water, another formula is used called exponential decay. In his analysis of the Miami case, Roll found that the physical distances PK-thrown objects traveled were directly related to Julio's physical proximity. A majority of the objects displaced by the PK were within a few feet of him, while more distant objects were affected to a lesser degree. This would tend to substantiate the theory that the Miami poltergeist radiated directly from Julio's body as it upheaved the glassware and other small objects in the warehouse. It was later found, however, that neither the movements of the poltergeist-projected missiles nor the distance they traveled followed the inverse square law but instead fit the exponential decay function better. This would suggest that some sort of nonphysical field was set up by Julio through which the poltergeistery moved.

Roll and his colleagues found the same principles at work when they reanalyzed their earlier data from the Seaford case. But they also found another principle at work which seemed to link the data they had collected from several other cases: PK-affected objects closest to the agent tended to travel short distances and move in a unified direction, while more distant objects traveled greater distances and in the opposite direction. A vortex follows this same principle. Could the poltergeist be a form of psychic vortex? This is only one question which Roll's data prompt us to ask.

What have Roll's researches told us about the poltergeist? The reader might be surprised when I say that, pioneering as they are, they still tell us very little. No one who is familiar with the range of effects the poltergeist can produce can fail to realize that the Miami and Seaford cases were relatively tame. They had none of the vehemence of the Wesley poundings, nor the range of phenomena the Bell Witch produced, nor even the persistence of the Bealings Bells. So one must ask, just how typical are the cases that Roll has investigated? Are they representative of the poltergeist at its most violent, or mere shadows of it?

Roll and his colleagues have indeed discovered many physical principles that seem to regulate the poltergeist. These patterns do seem to indicate that, during the typical "adolescent poltergeists," the focus-person is simply projecting his or her own PK locally in order to produce the disturbances. But these findings are based on cases which, to my mind, are not representative of the poltergeist in general. Actually Roll has in one way promulgated what I call "the poltergeist myth." This is the commonly held but mistaken notion that all poltergeists will center on a disturbed adolescent. Many investigators overlook the fact that many cases do not center on children. For instance, when W. E. Cox, a magician-turned-parapsychologist who formerly specialized in PK research at the Institute for Parapsychology at FRNM, made a comparative analysis of several reported poltergeists, he found that in 61 percent of them there was indeed a central agent who seemed instrumental to the poltergeist. However, no specific agent was found in 22 percent of the outbreaks and no children were present at all in many of them. Again one is led into a fantasy land of speculation. Could the "adolescent poltergeist" really be only one specific *type* of poltergeist?—and not a very forceful one at that? These are questions that I shall address later.

What about the fact that so many poltergeist agents seem to over-rely on such psychological defenses as denial and repression? Far from being a breakthrough, these facts tell us very little. They do help us to identify the psychological milieu that gives birth to the poltergeist, but this leaves many questions unanswered. Why do some people use PK as a vehicle of expression while others obviously cannot. Denial, repression, and sublimation are all defenses each of us uses every day. Yet poltergeists are rather rare. So it must go deeper than merely psychological frustration.

I also have to admit that I have doubts about putting too much stock in the "projected repression" theory. Perhaps this is really only a contributing factor leading to the outbreak of the poltergeist. It might not be the primary cause. In many cases investigators have been dealing with young children or adolescents on the verge of adulthood. I wonder: if you gave psychological tests to the next ten teen-agers you met on the street, how many of them would reveal the strong use of repression and denial in their test results? It comes right down to the "how big is big?" paradox. Since we have no baselines to judge how much denial and repression is normally used by an average teen-ager or young adult, we cannot accurately state how atypical Julio, Arnold, and other agents really are. Are they truly different from the "normal" teen-ager coping with today's troubled times?

There can be little doubt that the repression of hostility from conscious expression is a true characteristic of the poltergeist agent, but the poltergeist is just not that simple. Denied frustration seems to be a catalyzing cause, but not the primary causative ingredient of the poltergeist. Cases of poltergeists born from "projected repression" obviously do exist, but they are only a portion of the total picture. Even Roll's painstaking examination of the poltergeist had been based on only minor samplings of relatively weak types of PK effects. A locally projected PK force emanating from the body of a PK agent can explain how and why objects are moved and thrown. But what about reports of apports materializing in sealed rooms; or of paranormal fire-setting; or of stone-throwings; or apparitions and voices? We still have a long, long way to go before we understand these aspects of the poltergeist.

W. G. Roll has tried to demythologize the poltergeist and strip it of its supernatural aura. He has succeeded admirably with the "adolescent poltergeist." Now, admittedly, this type of "adolescent poltergeist" is probably the most common type, and it was through just such a case that I was first introduced to the complexities of the poltergeist as well as the psychodynamics behind it. I investigated the case in 1974 and eventually succeeded in witnessing the PK.

The report was brought to my attention by Raymond Bayless, who had been contacted about the case by a local newspaper. Apparently a Mrs. Downs, who lived in a suburban community near Los Angeles, had been calling the newspaper all week complaining that objects were being mysteriously hurled about her niece's house. The newspaper editors, while sensing a good story, really didn't know what to do about the case, so they decided to call in a professional investigator. Raymond immediately

called the family and they implored him to come out to
the house and see for himself what was going on. He, in
turn, asked me to join him.

The house was in a rather old, middle-class section of
town and was a somewhat rundown, two-story, rambling
affair. There was nothing unique about it, but in all my
years of investigating hauntings and the like I had never
seen such an odd sight as I did when I arrived on the scene
that day. An elderly white-haired woman was sitting on
the porch with an innocent-looking young girl beside
her. Another woman sat in a nearby car. This, I assumed,
was the distressed family. The teen-ager, whose name
was Chris, was the daughter of Mrs. Downs's niece, Mrs.
James. The whole family was terrified. They were even
afraid to go back into the house, Mrs. James told me. As
she fought back her tears, she ominously told me that the
"demons" were on the rampage again and tearing apart
the upstairs bedrooms.

Unfortunately Raymond had not arrived yet, so I tried
to calm the family. I assured them that no one would be
hurt by the "force," as I called it, and I tried to convince
them that outbreaks are not uncommon and that they
had nothing to do with spirits, especially evil ones. I also
told them that it would be all over before long. The
family seemed less frenzied after my explanation, and
everyone but Mrs. James went along with it. Mrs. Downs
and Chris escorted me inside through the kitchen door,
since the front door was locked (allegedly by the
poltergeist). Mrs. Downs was still scared, though, and
went only as far as the kitchen where she waited while
Chris took me through the hall to the living room. As we
walked along I could see broken objects strewn all
around. It looked more like a battle zone than a home.

Once inside the living room I heard a loud noise, as though something had been thrown against a wall upstairs. I looked at Chris, "Does the phenomenon ever make rapping noises?" I asked.

"Yes, it's throwing things," she answered nervously.

I went upstairs to look around while Chris, who had become extremely agitated by the noise, stayed below. Bedrooms opened out on both sides of the staircase. Broken objects were lying all over the beds and on the floors. So I went downstairs to ask Chris a few more questions. She was still standing in the living room where I had left her, but another "pop" sounded from upstairs as soon as I got to the foot of the stairs.

"Oh my God! It's starting again," shrieked Chris, half screaming, half crying, as she dashed out the front door. I then heard another sound from upstairs, but when I returned there was only an icy silence. Whatever was causing the disturbances was playing an elusive game with me. My attention, though, was just as much on Chris as on the poltergeist, since I thought she was the likely focus of the disturbances.

As I stood on the stairway landing, I heard the welcome voices of Raymond and his wife, Marjorie, who had just arrived. Marjorie assumed responsibility for calming the family, while Raymond came into the house to confer with me on the strategy we would adopt to investigate the case.

Since I wanted to talk with Raymond in private, we went upstairs. However, no sooner had we ascended the stairs and entered one of the bedrooms, than we heard something bouncing down the stairs. We immediately ran to the landing and saw a plastic container of hand cream at the foot of the staircase. Somehow it had been projected down the stairs. Mrs. Downs was in the living room, but she was very hard of hearing so apparently was not aware that anything had happened, and Chris was in the kitchen. The incident struck us as impressive but not conclusive, since we couldn't ascertain the exact positions of everyone in the house when it had occurred.

In the meantime Marjorie decided to go to the local supermarket to buy some food for the family, who hadn't eaten or slept in forty-eight hours. Not surprisingly, the well-being of the family became one of our main concerns throughout our investigation. After all, Raymond and I agreed, we had been called in to *help* the family, not to investigate them. So we were faced with a dual responsibility: first, to study the poltergeist as parapsychologists; and second, to work as counselors to help the family through the ordeal they were facing as best we could.

We had hardly begun to discuss these issues when another crash, this time an explosively loud bang, resounded right next to us. I ran to the landing with Raymond close behind, and watched a six-inch glass bottle bounce down the stairs. It had apparently initially struck against the heater at the top of the stairs and had then tumbled down them. From the kitchen where the family had gathered we could hear their muffled cries. They too had heard the noise.

Unfortunately this incident transpired before Raymond and I had had time to work out the plans of our investigational strategy, so again the family was not under our surveillance at the moment of the incident. However, if any one of them *had* thrown the bottle, he or she probably would have been seen running from the living room by the other family members or by us.

My hearing is acute and I didn't hear anyone scurrying about immediately before or after the incident. Nothing of any consequence happened in the house for over an hour.

Marjorie returned with some bread and cold cuts as seven o'clock rolled by. We joined the family in the kitchen and convinced them during the meal that, although what they were going through was frightening, the disturbances were harmless and would soon burn out. It was clear to us that tensions within the family were acute and the psychological situation extremely sensitive. The family expected some sort of explanation for the phenomena from us, so we reiterated our firm belief that no spirits were "haunting" their house and that no harm would befall them. We compared the situation to an overcharged battery discharging itself. (We did not feel that this was the right time to explain the nature of the poltergeist to them, since such an explanation would probably just add to their confusion and fears.) By this time it was getting dark, and since the family told us that few disturbances occurred during the night (although at first they had), Raymond and his wife left to find a nearby hotel room for the next few days. I stayed behind to talk with the family.

But a half hour later the calm that had settled over the family disintegrated. In a way, though, the incident that caused the ensuing pandemonium was the first one that proved that the poltergeist was at least partly genuine.

It was 9:05 and I was in the living room sitting on a couch that faced directly into the hall and stairwell. Mrs. Downs was right beside me, while Mrs. James was standing opposite us at the hallway entrance. Chris was squatting on her haunches beside her mother. They were looking nervously at me as I tried to cheer them up with some humorous stories about some of my other psychic adventures. All of a sudden a tremendous explosion sounded from the hallway. The noise obviously came from the middle of the passage. Mrs. James screamed and ran into the living room while I rushed into the hallway to investigate. There I found the cause of the noise. A plastic compact case had apparently hurled itself out of the bathroom and had smashed against the hallway wall. It was open, undamaged, with the powder puff lying by the bathroom door two feet away.

The entire incident was an enigma. Since no one was in the bathroom, I could definitely say that none of the household could have thrown the object. I would have seen any such trickery. Furthermore, the noise made by the crash was very loud, and I could barely reproduce it by slamming my fist against the wall as hard as I could. None of the family members could have produced the noise while in my direct view. The location of the compact itself also presented somewhat of a mystery. The object struck with such obvious force (judging by the sound it made) that it should have been smashed to pieces. Yet it wasn't even chipped. And if the object had been thrown normally, it should have bounced back *away* from the wall. But it hadn't. I found it lying right at the foot of the wall.*

Again the family was in an uproar. I had to pacify them but I also had a more immediate problem to cope

* Such enigmas are typical of the poltergeist and many investigators have been puzzled by these same paradoxes. For example, objects may be thrown with tremendous force, yet will not break. Glasses often fall from cupboards onto hard floors but remain unshattered. Our poltergeist was following this stereotype.

with. Mrs. James was beginning to worry that someone
in the house would be maimed by the broken glass or
flying objects, and I had to assure her otherwise. I pointed
out to her and the family that, in the entire history of the
poltergeist, no serious injury had ever been caused. To be
sure, people may get thumped by flying objects, I advised
her, but usually they bounce off harmlessly even if they
are projected at high speed. (I didn't tell them that a few
injuries actually have been reported.)

Mrs. Downs, Chris, and Mrs. James huddled around
the kitchen table as we spoke. To lighten the mood, I told
them a brief story about W. G. Roll's investigation of
some object-throwings in Newark, New Jersey. He too
had advised the family not to be alarmed, since
poltergeist-projected objects rarely hit anybody. As soon
as he said these fateful words, he reported, a bottle had
come flying through the air and rapped him on his head!

The family got a good laugh at the story, and since the
tension seemed to be easing a bit, I left the kitchen to see
if I could determine the exact trajectory the compact had
traveled when it had shot out of the bathroom a few
minutes before. This didn't take long, but as I walked
back into the living room to write up some notes the next
PK incident occurred. It was a curious incident to say the
least. I had just passed the kitchen entryway and had
noted that all the family members were sitting talking to
one another. I had just entered the living room when
something struck my left pocket. Looking down, I saw a
small bottle top bounce off my thigh and fall to the floor a
foot away. I could still hear the family talking in the
kitchen, so apparently they were unaware of what had
happened. I doubted one of them had thrown the
object—but it *was* possible, since my back was turned at
the time.

This incident marked the end of the PK activity for quite awhile. Later that evening a bottle crashed in the kitchen, but Chris was the only witness and could easily have broken it herself. This bit of breakage ended the poltergeistery for the day and, at the family's request, Raymond, who returned a bit later, and I bedded down for the night in the living room.

As the first day of our investigation ended, it was clear that we had a typical poltergeist on our hands. Chris was the obvious focus of the attack and already, without much difficulty, we could see the deep hostilities which obsessed her and which were the probable root of the PK outburst. It was clear that she was having problems dealing with her relatives, especially her aunt, and was also overly preoccupied with her own rapidly emerging sexuality. She was thriteen, but could have easily passed for seventeen. In fact she took pride in looking older than her years. But she had been the butt of many cruel jokes by her schoolmates because of her mature development.

While Raymond and I discussed these issues the next morning, the family arose one by one from their first good night's sleep in two weeks. By 11:30 A.M. everyone was up, including Chris. We were instantly on guard when she came downstairs for breakfast, since we knew that the poltergeist would probably awaken with her. An hour later, as we expected, the poltergeist made its presence known. Raymond and I were in the living room when we heard a bang from the kitchen where Mrs. James and Chris were fixing breakfast. Mrs. James lost control and started screaming that she wasn't going to stay in the house any longer. We looked around the kitchen, but never could really determine what had caused the noise.

The next incident occurred an hour later, but by this

time we were ready for it and had every member of the
family under complete control. I was sitting on the couch,
with Chris sitting on a chair cater-cornered to it on my
right at the time. Mrs. Downs and Mrs. James were in the
kitchen with Raymond, who was standing at the kitchen
door with his back to the hall. Everyone was quiet
when—cling!—we all heard a metallic sound as a spoon
bounced off the open hallway door and fell into the living
room. Chris hadn't so much as flinched. It was an
impressive instance of psychokinesis.

The spoon incident introduced about two hours of
object-throwings. It seemed that the entire house was
under siege as object after object hurled about in virtually
every room in the house. It was complete pandemonium
and, with the house occupants running about in fright, it
was impossible to tell where everyone was when each
incident occurred. So, despite the fact that the poltergeist
was extremely active, we could not verify which of its
apparent actions were genuine. However, one incident
was particularly impressive to me. I had run to a back
room where a container had popped off a shelf. I was
alone in the room recording the incident in my notebook,
facing the only doorway leading into the room when
suddenly I heard a small object bash into the wall behind
me. I didn't see the object in flight, but definitely heard
something strike the wall and fall. Unfortunately, since
there was so much debris strewn about the room, it was
impossible to determine just what had been thrown.

By 4:12 the object-throwing had subsided considerably. But one isolated incident occurred at this time that I
found just as impressive as the one cited above.

Just before this incident took place, Mrs. James had
once again expressed her concern about the possibility

that she might be hurt by the flying objects. So I advised her to go into her bedroom and close the door. There, I assured her, she would be safe. However, I had secret motives for giving her this advice. It conveniently got Mrs. James out of the way, so to speak, since I wanted to keep Chris under close supervision. After all, I could not dismiss the possibility that Chris was faking at least some of the poltergeistery. So, with Mrs. James and Mrs. Downs (who was outside) accounted for, I could keep watch over Chris who was in the kitchen with me. Just a few moments after Mrs. James was settled in her room, Chris and I heard a loud wooden knock next to us. On checking, we found that a bottle of fingernail polish had been thrown against the back bedroom door. The room in question was on the same side of the hall as the kitchen. Admittedly I had been distracted at the crucial moment, since I was about to make a phone call (the phone was on the kitchen table), but Chris could not have got past me, thrown the object, and returned without my seeing her. However, the telekinetic activity wasn't over yet. Chris went to calm her mother, and while Chris was comforting her we all clearly heard glass shattering. A vase on the dresser had been smashed against the wall.

Eventually everything settled down again, and by 5:45 P.M. it looked as though the poltergeist had abated. Indeed it died out as mysteriously as it had been born. The end of the poltergeist was also evident when Marjorie saw Chris deliberately kick an object and then claim that the poltergeist had done it. This incident occurred just after Marjorie had told the girl that, now that the PK was over, she would have to go back to school. (She had been absent throughout the case.)

Since it looked as though the disturbances were now

over, Marjorie, Raymond, and I began the slow process of talking with the family, learning their needs and goals, joys and frustrations. When by 8:30 P.M., nothing untoward had occurred we were further relieved to think that perhaps the storm was over. But, if the poltergeist's fury had been exorcised, another kind of storm was just brewing as the family members, frustrated and puzzled by the whole affair, began verbally to express their deep-seated anger toward each other. For the first time, it seemed, the family was able to discuss their true feelings toward one another. Could this have vanquished the poltergeist?

I stayed with the family all the next afternoon. Midday was usually the critical period, since that was when the poltergeist had habitually erupted during its short life, but the hours came and went in silence. At 3:30 P.M. Chris cajoled Raymond into a game of Monopoly and I gathered up my notes and started on the long drive home. Raymond stayed to complete the family's readjustment. The poltergeist was over and so was our investigation.*

How much of the poltergeistery we witnessed during our investigation was genuine, and how much could have been faked by Chris? These are questions that are difficult to answer. I am convinced that during our stay I

---

*A few weeks later I was called back to the house when Mrs. James reported the recurrence of some minor PK disturbances. As soon as I entered the house and went into the living room accompanied by Mrs. Downs, I heard an object thrown in the kitchen. Mrs. Downs heard nothing. Moments later Chris and her mother came out of the bedroom, so neither of them could have made the noise. Mrs. Downs entered the kitchen and called to me to join her. She pointed to a bottle of fingernail polish which was sitting in the sink. She said she had no idea how it got there. The incident was very impressive.

witnessed genuine PK and had therefore verified the poltergeist. But to what extent Chris was responsible for faking some of the incidents I just cannot say. It is my belief that serious fraud probably began the second day of our investigation. I feel just as sure that much of what we witnessed during the first day was genuine. But even today I turn the memories of this poltergeist over and over in my mind trying to sort fact from fraud. My only recourse is to sit and wait for another case to investigate.

The case of Mrs. James and her troubled family is fairly typical. The type of PK we observed and the psychological setting tally remarkably well with what W. G. Roll has observed. This leads me to believe that the poltergeist may well be a universal phenomenon.

But, apart from the metapsychology of the poltergeist, this case also offers several insights into the psychology of fraud. Just why do so many children, as Roll as well as other poltergeist investigators have discovered, begin deliberately faking and imitating the poltergeist?

There are several psychological reasons why poltergeist children so often resort to fraud. Often a poltergeist is an outgrowth of repressed hostilities and family tension, usually centering on a child around the age of puberty. The agent is usually not even aware that he or she is the cause of the disturbances, probably because the subconscious takes over so completely. But in some cases the person will betray an unusual type of intuitive inkling that he or she is instrumental to the poltergeist.

What has this to do with fakery? In order to relieve frustrations, the child will often start to manufacture incidents impulsively in order to display more directly the locked up emotions that have engendered the poltergeist in the first place. Second, children do like to pull pranks and the poltergeist often serves as a perfect cover-up. Third, during the outbreak the child usually begins to receive the attention that had been denied in the past and which was a contributing factor (frustration) to the onset of the poltergeist. The disturbances become ego-satisfying and a means of gaining attention. And last, the child, confounded and burdened by the frustration, probably does have an inner urge to strike out or "displace" his or her aggression and may be compelled to fake in answer to a subconscious or only vaguely conscious need. For instance, in one case investigated by W. G. Roll, the agent was caught red-handed throwing an object. Yet when he was questioned on a polygraph about the incident, the boy denied it and the lie-detector indicated that the boy believed he was telling the truth. This unexpected finding suggested to Roll that sometimes a child might commit fraud unconsciously or when in an abnormal state of mind and so doesn't even remember having done it.

W. G. Roll and other investigators in the United States are not the only parapsychologists who have been making strides in understanding the poltergeist. Parapsychologists in Europe, especially Germany, have also been fascinated in recent years by the combined psychological and parapsychological puzzle of the poltergeist.

Professor Hans Bender at the University of Freiburg, West Germany, has also been investigating poltergeists for several years. Like Roll, he has observed many typical adolescent poltergeists, but he has also been able to witness some of the more uncanny aspects and manifestations. His work has revealed some of the cultural influences that can affect the poltergeist. When witchcraft and enchantment were thought to be the cause, the PK agents often vomited pins (an old witchcraft tradition), and "animal familiars" were seen. These occurrences have not been recorded in modern times. When witnesses thought that demons caused the disturbances, the poltergeist acted accordingly. Yet these manifestations of the poltergeist, i.e., "speaking," have not been reported for many decades. That Bender has encountered different types of cases in Europe from those Roll has found in the United States is therefore predictable. Different cultures may give rise to different types of poltergeists. Although the poltergeist has a worldwide reputation for object-throwing and for generally being a hellish nuisance, two of Bender's recent cases exhibited an astonishing array of effects of a type not reported in any contemporary American accounts.

I can clearly recall the stir these cases made when Bender reported them to the Parapsychological Association in 1969. The convention was meeting in one of New York's higher-priced hotels and was crowded with investigators from all over the world. The convention had so far rendered us glassy-eyed with reports of statistics, card-guessing, and computer analyses. Bender took to the podium in the midst of all this. He is an extremely tall man and is fluent in many languages besides his native German, and holds degrees in medicine and philosophy as well as in psychology. He fits the typical "mad scientist" image rather well, and he talked enthusiastically as he leaned forward while speaking. As soon as he began his fifty-minute presentation, glassy eyes quickly turned to attentive stares. The reality of the poltergeist was still a hotly contested issue in 1969 and few contemporary firsthand eyewitness testimonies from reliable parapsychologists were on record. This type of report had just begun to filter into the association a few years before. (In fact, it was during this same convention that Roll reported seeing the levitating table at Olive Hill, see p. 108).

Even before Bender had investigated the two major cases that highlighted his convention report, he was well aware of the more bizarre powers of the poltergeist. As he explained in his address, in 1948 a Bavarian couple from the village of Vachendorf had reported a poltergeist to Freiburg University and he had followed it up. Playing cards disappeared and reappeared in odd places. The couple and their fourteen-year-old daughter were bombarded by everything from stones to work tools as they lay in bed. The oddest phenomenon reported during the case was the inexplicable teleportation of objects. At one time the mistress of the house collected all the poltergeist-teleported items, which had been scattered helter-skelter during a previous bombardment, and placed them in a toolbox. Then she sat on the box in defiance of the poltergeist. Yet, even as she did so, the same items that she had so carefully locked away started dropping down from the ceiling, in front of her. They were soon scattered all over the floor. The witness thereupon opened the toolbox, only to find it empty.

In 1951 a Catholic priest from Neusatz called Bender in on a case where a poltergeist was tormenting an old woman and her thirty-year-old retarded son. Linen had been torn up, food had been hurled about, large objects had disappeared from the house, and the tails of horses in the stable had been tied in braids.

These are only two of the cases Bender had behind

him when the Rosenheim poltergeist came to his attention in 1967–1968.

This case did not take place in a family dwelling, but in a fashionable law office. At first inexplicable mechanical and electrical failures and malfunctions disrupted the office. Neon lights went out; bulbs were unscrewed from their sockets, while many more exploded; fuses were blown; strange sounds resounded throughout the rooms. The telephone system went haywire next. Phone calls that had never been made were registered to the office and oftentimes specific phones in the office were singled out as the source of the disturbance. Witnesses at first thought that the wiring was at fault, so a voltage magnifier was attached to the voltage main to monitor any disturbance. But this apparatus showed odd deflections during the height of the outbreak, as though it were malfunctioning. The maintenance department of the phone company, which was carrying out the investigation, could not understand the problem. Finally they installed an emergency power unit in order to bypass any problem in the normal power system, but the malfunctions went on as before.

Usually a parapsychologist is called into a poltergeist case only when the witnesses have been unable to find any normal cause for the disturbances. Bender was summoned to the scene after electrical experts failed to pin down the cause of the Rosenheim problem, and in true poltergeist tradition he found that the disturbances only occurred when a nineteen-year-old employee named Annemarie came in to work. Lighting fixtures were actually seen to swing behind her as she walked through the office. Bender eventually theorized that the disturbances to the electrical equipment had little to do with electrical malfunction. As he reported to the convention:

Two physicists, Dr. J. Karger and Dr. G. Zicha, controlled the main's voltage variations, electrostatic charging, external static, magnetic fields, loose contacts, ultrasonic and infrasonic effects from vibrations, and last but not least, manual intervention and deceit, and came to the conclusion that no possible normal explanation could be found. They disconnected the monitoring device of the electrical circuit and supplied it by a 1.5 volt battery—the deflection continued. Some unknown mechanical influence without apparent cause had acted on the pointer of the monitoring instruments. Thus PK was objectively demonstrated.

Later more conventional poltergeistery broke out at the Rosenheim office, as though the phenomena were escalating.

I don't find it odd that, once the paranormal nature of the disturbances were isolated and verified, the poltergeist changed its "strategy." All through the study of the poltergeist we have seen how fickle it is. If it is called a demon, it readily assumes the role. If it is treated as an intelligent entity, it will rap coherently in answer to questions. Treat it as a witch, and it will give you animal familiars. Apparently the poltergeist is extremely sensitive to the attitudes and beliefs of those witnessing it. The Rosenheim poltergeist didn't act like a bona-fide poltergeist until the witnesses realized what they were confronting. As soon as Bender verified that they were dealing with a genuine poltergeist, the nature of the PK changed. Objects shifted position and pictures rotated on walls in true poltergeist fashion. Annemarie even started revealing symptoms of hysteria. It was almost as though the poltergeist had suddenly realized how it was *supposed* to act. Bender hoped eventually to control the PK forces which had been let loose in the office by hypnotizing Annemarie, but her parents would not allow it. However, one odd fact did show up later during the investigation. Although a poor PK subject when experimentally tested, Annemarie showed exceptional ESP ability. This sparked Bender's curiosity, since he had tested a fifteen-year-old "poltergeist boy" two years prior who had also shown excellent ESP ability. After leaving her job at the law office, Annemarie found other employment and some residual PK broke out there as well but soon abated.

Shortly after the Rosenheim case ended, Bender personally confronted that mystery among mysteries—teleportation*—during an investigation in Nickelheim. This town is only ten miles distant from the town of Rosenheim. For four months in 1968 and 1969 a worker, his wife, and their thirteen-year-old daughter, Brigitte, had been disturbed by mysterious knockings on the doors and windows of their house, and by stone-throwings inside and outside their home. The poltergeist intensified: objects flew about, eggs were cracked over the heads of visitors, clothing was ripped, and Brigitte's dolls were placed in lewd positions. Many of the incidents suggested the actual teleportation of physical objects through physical matter.

"At the very moment that a priest blessed the house," Bender reported, "a stone fell from the ceiling and came to rest on a board without any bouncing almost as if it

---

* Teleportation can be defined as the transportation of matter through other matter, or the dematerialization and rematerialization of matter from one place to another.

were fastened to a magnet. The priest picked it up and it gave the sensation of being warm."

I think this statement deserves special comment, since these observations are consistent with yet another semiconsistent pattern to which the poltergeist adheres. Teleported and apported objects are not *always* found to be warm when handled, but this observation has been repeated in so many cases and from so many different lands, that it deserves to be considered a true poltergeist characteristic. Why are these objects so peculiarly warm? I can think of two very different explanations. Any object that has undergone physical transformation is going to be affected by energy; and since energy and heat are linked physically, one might expect that PK-affected objects would become hot during the process of manipulation. On the other hand, of course, the skeptic could argue that a fraudulently thrown object would be warmed by the hand that held it. However, I think that we can safely say that the warmth generated by apported objects is probably telling us something fundamental about the physical process involved during the act of teleportation. But just what it is telling us can only be a matter of conjecture.

During the Nickelheim case, objects also suddenly vanished from inside the house only to be found later, deposited outside. One witness even attempted deliberately to demonstrate the poltergeist's ability to apport objects out of the house. As Bender reported:

He put bottles containing perfume and tablets on the kitchen table, asked the inhabitants of the house to go outside, closed all the windows and doors, and then left himself. After a short time, the perfume bottle appeared in the air outside the house, and a bit later on, the bottle of tablets appeared in the air at the height of the roof and fell to the ground in a zigzag manner.

Many poltergeist witnesses have noted that PK-manipulated objects sometimes do not travel in normal trajectories. Instead they often make inexplicable curves, even 90-degree angles, move at irregular speeds, and exhibit other bizarre motions. This, in fact, is yet another common characteristic of the poltergeist.

With this background on the case, Bender and his Freiburg team paid a visit to the town in order to carry out their own investigations.

Arriving at the disturbed house and talking with some of the witnesses, the investigators tried to encourage the poltergeist to act up for them. They even placed objects in a sealed cupboard, for if the PK could move these items it would prove that the PK could act *through* physical barriers. But nothing happened until several days later, when the family excitedly reported to the Freiburg team that when they were away some of the target items sealed in the cupboard had teleported out of it. Bender found that the seal which secured the cupboard was still intact, but one member of the team discovered a way to slacken the glass panels and edge out the objects. Failures, however, are often followed by success. While Bender's rather contrived matter-through-matter test was inconclusive, a personal experience more than made up for it. At the time of this incident, Bender was with the entire family in the kitchen. He had hung his coat in an adjacent wardrobe. Brigitte's mother had gone to the door when suddenly she ran back, calling to Bender, "Your coat is outside the house carefully laid in the snow beside the staircase." Indeed it was. The whole family had been under Bender's observation at the time, except for the mother, who had been gone for only eight seconds. (A tape recorder was monitoring the family and a check back to the tape proved the length of time the mother had been gone.) Tests proved that it would have taken at least twenty seconds for anyone in the house to place the coat outside the house and in the position in which it was found. Bender also photographed the outstretched coat and his snapshot is just as revealing as his written account of the incident. The coat is carefully laid and folded on a bed of snow, yet there is *not a single footstep* or any other disturbance in the snow around it.

No doubt impressed by the coat incident, Bender built a special control box guarded by a camera into which household objects could be placed and left it in the house. He hoped that the poltergeist would disrupt the target objects inside and be photographed in the act. But by this time the poltergeist activity was clearly on the wane and only one sealed-in object ultimately toppled. Also more and more visitors were parading through the house and Brigitte and a friend began to fake the disturbances by throwing and moving things about. This was a clear sign to Bender that the case was over.

Based on the findings from his own research, Bender has come to a novel conclusion about the source of the energy released during the poltergeist attack. He believes that, while most of the outbreaks do center on a specific agent who is often pathologically disturbed, the force is more powerful than anything that could be housed within the body. For example, the force behind the Rosenheim poltergeist once moved a 400-pound storage cabinet. The movement of matter-through-matter would also require a superhuman amount of energy. Consequently Bender suggests that the poltergeist agent may not *project* PK energy so much as organize energy from normal sources through PK. This energy would then be rerouted in order to "feed" the poltergeist with the power it needs.

For several years a few psychical researchers have toyed with the idea that the poltergeist force may not be wholly projected from the body but may be generated by the subject who is actually manipulating or making psychic use of random energy sources. There are some data which readily support this theory. Andrew Robertson, a physicist friend of poltergeist expert Harry Price, once calculated that if one cubic foot of air is cooled one degree in temperature, it loses fifteen foot-pounds of energy. (A foot-pound of energy is the expenditure needed to move a fifteen-pound object one foot.) Cooling the atmosphere would release a ready source of energy, which could be redirected by and as PK. But this "explanation" really doesn't explain anything at all, since we still have to fathom the process by which the subject exerts his PK on the atmosphere in order to cool it in the first place. So, while we may have some idea of where the energy for the poltergeist comes from, we still don't know what the mechanics of this energy transformation are. Nonetheless, evidence supporting this intriguing and useful theory has been found during some laboratory PK tests, as the following two examples illustrate.

In 1973 Dr. Gertrude Schmeidler of the City University of New York published the results of an experiment she conducted with Ingo Swann, a well-known psychic, which was designed to determine whether or not he could use PK to alter the temperature readings on delicate thermistors situated several feet away from him. She found that Swann could indeed single out one thermistor from a group and use PK to increase or decrease its temperature. However, this is not all the psychologist discovered. A post-hoc analysis indicated that while the thermistor upon which Swann was concentrating did change temperature, other thermistors distant from it changed temperature also but in the opposite direction. This suggests that energy was being taken from these outlying areas and redirected to affect the target thermistor.

Harry Price made a similar finding back in the 1920s when he was testing Stella C., a famous medium, in his laboratory in London. Stella C. could produce table levitations and could make objects in sealed cages move about. During these PK performances the temperature in the room decreased by several degrees. (Price even installed thermometers and photographed them periodically during the séances.)

The power behind the poltergeist becomes more comprehensible when one thinks of the size of a normal room and the energy lost if its temperature were lowered by only one degree. Why haven't poltergeist investigators noticed this phenomenon if it generally occurs? Probably because investigators hardly would be expected to notice such a slight temperature change in a room. Yet a drop of just one degree *could* account for the power behind many poltergeists.

The Freiburg team has also tried to determine the psychological setting that breeds the poltergeist. In this respect their research has followed Roll's procedures. Bender has been fortunate enough to have investigated several active cases, and John Mischo, his colleague at the

Institut für Grenzgebiete der Psychologie und Psychohygiene, has made in-depth psychological evaluations of two poltergeist agents. In both instances the subjects had unstable personality structures. They were irritable and emotionally infantile; that is, impulsive and in need of instant gratification with no ability to tolerate frustration. Concern over social esteem and sexuality were causes for anxiety, and they both tended to display aggression. They demonstrated excessive repression and projection, and would not acknowledge conflicts. They also believed that they did not live up to the social demand for personal efficiency required of them. This factor only aggravated the unrealistic demand for social esteem they felt. Mischo believed that these factors, as well as both subjects' feelings of inferiority, caused the conflicts that had released the poltergeists. It is evident that Mischo's findings closely parallel those of Roll when evaluating American poltergeist agents.

In all the cases outlined in this chapter, the poltergeist agents were apparently unaware of their own complicity in the production of the events. This naïveté may be more apparent than real, for there actually is some evidence that poltergeist agents do vaguely realize that they are the cause of the disturbances. Some of them appear to be much less defiant or fearful of the poltergeist than might be expected. They sometimes confess to faking the disturbances, even when it could be proved that they could not have faked them. For example, in 1964 a poltergeist broke up a court reporter's office in Oakland. As in the Rosenheim case, the first PK incidents mimicked electrical malfunctions. Typewriters went haywire and the live buttons on the telephones flashed on and off even when the phones were not in use.

Finally office machinery and furniture were thrown about furiously. A young and recently married man named John Orfanides was in the center of the case. When questioned by the police, he gave them a complete confession, much to the relief of the officials. But he never could explain how he had managed to throw all the furniture about without being seen. Did he confess under police pressure? Or was he compelled to confess because of a subconscious knowledge that he was actually responsible for the poltergeist?

4

Stone-Throwing Attacks

I put my bullsack and mosquito netting on the wooden floor and soon fell asleep. At about one o'clock at night I half awoke, hearing something fall near my head outside the mosquito curtain on the floor. After a couple of minutes I completely awoke and turned my head half around to see what was falling on the floor. They were *black stones* from 1/8 to 2/3 of an inch long. I got out of the curtain and turned up the keresene lamp that was standing on the floor at the foot of the bed. I saw then that the stones were falling through the roof in a parabolic line. They fell on the floor close to my head-pillow. I went out and awoke the boy (a Malay-Pelambang coolie) whoe was sleeping on the floor in the next room. I told him to go outside and examine the jungle up to a certain distance. He did so whilst I lighted up the jungle a little by means of a small "ever-ready" electric lantern. At the same time that my boy was outside the stones did not stop falling. My boy came in again, and I told him to search the kitchen to see if anybody could be there. He went to the kitchen and I went inside the room again to watch the stones falling down. I knelt down near the head of my bed and tried to catch the stones while they were falling through the air towards me, but I could never catch them; it seemed to me that they *changed their direction* in the air as soon as I tried to get hold of them. I could not catch any of them before they fell to the floor. Then I climbed up the partition-wall between my room and the boy's and examined the roof just above it from which the stones were flying. They came right through the "kadjang" but there were no holes in the Kadjang. When I tried to catch them there at the very spot of coming out, I also failed.

This extract is part of an eyewitness account of a stone-throwing poltergeist which lasted for only one night in the jungles of Sumatra around the turn of the century. The reporter, a Dutch traveler named W. G. Grottendieck, also noted that the stones fell abnormally slowly, as though they were hovering in the air, and hit the ground with an inexplicably loud bang. They were also warm to the touch. As the entire house was surrounded by jungle, Grottendieck was totally mystified by the occurrence, since no one could be seen throwing the stones.

Stone-throwing is one of the poltergeist's most common activities. If you recall, Hans Bender came across stone-throwings during his Nickelheim case. Stone-throwing poltergeists can be diversified. Sometimes the rocks will bombard the outside of a house, or sometimes, as in the Sumatra case, the inside. Some poltergeists only throw stones, while in other cases stone-peltings augment rappings and object-tossings. Stone-throwing poltergeists do not always exhibit traditional poltergeist behavior. For example, they do not necessarily focus on only one individual living in the affected house; and they may even attack a home after the original occupants have left. They are usually brief outbursts, though. The rocks themselves are sometimes found to be warm to the touch (similar to the heat-generating apported items I spoke about previously) and will often follow odd trajectories.

As I have emphasized in earlier chapters, the poltergeist does more than merely spend its time banging on walls or displacing objects. A discussion of stone-throwing outbreaks, therefore, is a good place to begin to explore the poltergeist's more complicated behavior. Stone-throwing poltergeists seem guided by a limited intelligence. In other words, there seems to be a form of motivation or cognition on the part of the force engendering the PK. This is illustrated in the following case, which was reported by the famous naturalist Ivan Sanderson.

Sanderson confronted the poltergeist while visiting Sumatra in 1928. He had been invited to a party of sorts and was sitting on a veranda when small rocks started to pelt down on the deck. The host explained to his astonished guests that these rock-throwings were very common, and that if the rocks were marked and thrown away the very same pebbles would be hurled back again within a few minutes. This was an amazing claim, since any stones thrown from the porch would fall into extremely thick vegetation. Nevertheless, the guests marked the stones with lipstick, files, and chalk and, as Sanderson reports, "We all threw them back hard or lightly in every conceivable direction. Almost but not quite all of the marked stones came back onto the verandah within a matter of seconds, a few some minutes later."

Some sort of intelligent force obviously lay behind this poltergeist, for it had the ability to track down the pebbles and identify them almost instantly. This case also illustrates my personal contention that the poltergeist seems to have a will and personality of its own (the Miami and Seaford cases do not suggest this, however). Many poltergeist attacks seem organized, well planned, and give evidence of a definite purpose and plan of disruption. At times the poltergeist will show a clear awareness of what it is doing. For example, in the Sanderson case the poltergeist could easily have thrown any stone close at hand, but it didn't. Instead it teleported stones that had been specially marked.

Stone-throwings are not only one of the most common types of poltergeist effects, they are also the most universal. Earlier I mentioned that many historical poltergeist reports are highlighted with vivid accounts of animal apparitions, chattering poltergeists, apports, and the like. These effects mirrored the cultural beliefs and expectations of the time. Naturally we can assume that the poltergeist is influenced by the culture in which it is manifested. But stone-throwing poltergeists are some-what different in this respect. Their basic pattern of disruption has not changed over the centuries, even though they have occurred in different countries and in different eras. For instance, in A.D. 530 it was recorded that Deacon Helpidium, physician to King Theodoric of the Ostrogoths suffered from a diabolic infestation that caused showers of stones to fall in his house. Grimm, in his *Teutonic Mythologie*, records a case dating back to A.D. 856 in Kembden. Rappings, voices, and showers of stones plagued the unfortunate victim's home. Stone-throwing poltergeists were still active during the Renaissance. One such case spoke of a pagan who, after converting to Christianity, was startled to see objects floating about his house while stones mysteriously fell upon it. Another old report dating back to 1659 records how soldiers who were guarding the Monastery of Malbroun were powerless to stop mysterious outbreaks of fire in the building. They also watched helplessly as covers were torn from beds, and stones were thrown throughout the monastery. I could go on and on.* Even today, from time to time, the newspapers report stories about houses that are attacked by mysterious rock bombardments.

Stone-throwings represent only one of many types of PK effects employed during the disturbances. Eventually the poltergeist may begin to throw other things than rocks and pebbles. A typical stone-throwing poltergeist of this type was witnessed in 1921 in a provincial French village by the local clergyman, M. Laval, whose account was printed in Camille Flammarion's *Haunted Houses*. The outbreak focused on a local farmer. The stones first began to pelt his house in September and continued for months, being most intense in October. They fell day and night, even following the man when he went out in the open fields. No one actually *saw* them traveling; they just appeared out of the air and hovered in the sky before they struck the house. (The farmer's three children were watched by investigators all the while to make sure they were not to blame.) M. Laval first looked into the strange goings-on at the request of the farmer who sought his advice, and during his stay he saw a rock appear mysteriously and strike one of the children. Later he was struck by a rock himself, although he was fifty-two yards from the house. He also noted that the stones often fell slowly, and were rarely seen at high altitudes. Usually they were seen approximately six feet up in the air before they struck their target. Soon after Laval arrived on the

* The full accounts of these cases may be found by consulting Hereward Carrington and Nandor Fodor, *Haunted People* (New York: Dutton, 1951).

scene the poltergeist changed its tactics and began throwing apples from outside the house.

Even in relatively modern times, people plagued by anything paranormal tend to call for the local priest before turning to the scientist. It is for this reason that some of the most clearly reported poltergeist cases have come from clergymen who have witnessed the infestations at firsthand. One such case was reported by Father Aldhelm Bowring, who witnessed a poltergeist in 1934 while stationed in the West Indies. In this case, though, the first observers were the police.

The rock-throwings were first reported in September in the *West Indian*. The newspaper reported that the police had even climbed on top of the house hoping to find someone responsible for the bombardment, but the stones kept falling onto the roof before their eyes. When they hit, the story continued, they didn't bounce as they should have if tossed normally, but lay still as though glued to the roof as soon as they struck. Some of them weighed as much as a pound. Nonetheless the police insisted that a prankster was responsible for the disturbance, since a member of the family had been threatened in the past by anonymous letters. But no prankster was found, even though the stone-throwings continued unabated. The stone attacks focused on a particular member of the household: Dolly Woodroffe, aged twenty. In fact, the stones usually fell on that part of the roof directly over her bedroom. Sometimes the projectiles were not stones but bits of food, glass, gravel, and other small items.

Another mysterious phenomenon witnessed by a family member was a human-like apparition:

One night in September last I was inside the house with my grandmother, and my two aunts...and I heard something fall on the house. My grandmother told me to look out and see if there was anyone in the road. I looked out and saw a white man in the road about 12 feet away.

The child pointed out the figure to her grandmother, who could not see it. As her report continues:

That same night several stones fell on the house before I went to bed. While stones were falling the man was there, but I did not see him throwing any. The stones continued falling for more than a month, day and night. Sometimes stones would fall inside the house even when it was closed. Every time the stones were falling I used to see the man.... I pointed the man out to several persons, including the police but they all said they did not see anything.

In this case the stone-throwings heralded more violent telekinetic upheavals. Chairs, irons, and tables were all tossed about the house. During their investigation, detectives hid on the grounds looking for the person responsible for the mischief, but without success. "When stones fell on the roof they remained there and did not fall to the ground," a detective reported to Father Bowring. "I remember one morning I was inside the house and the doors and windows were all closed. I heard a sound on the galvanized roof and a stone fell in front of me without making or leaving any hole."

According to Father Bowring's report, the stone-throwing lasted for two months until the family finally moved out. The house caught fire shortly afterward and was completely gutted.

The prevalence of stone-throwing poltergeists is no better illustrated than by the fact that two cases were reported in California during the early 1960s, one in a large city and one in the lake resort of Big Bear. In each case many witnesses, including the police, observed the incidents, and one case subsequently ended in a most unusual courtroom drama. Both cases were investigated by Raymond Bayless, who was to play a significant role in the court proceedings. Raymond, who first taught me the techniques of poltergeist investigation, has spent more time in tracking down rock-throwing poltergeists than any other contemporary investigator. Although he reported on both these cases in *The Enigma of the Poltergeist*, which was published in 1967, he turned over his private files to me in 1975, from which I have drawn the following summaries and evaluations.

First word of the Big Bear poltergeist came by way of the *Los Angeles Times* when it ran an article on November 10, 1962, about unexplained stone-throwing centering on a house in Big Bear City, California. (Big Bear is a mountain resort near Lake Arrowhead, an hour's drive from Los Angeles proper.) The article reported that stones had been mysteriously dropping from the sky onto a local residence for four months, and that the sheriff's deputies who had been called in to investigate could find no explanation. One of these investigators even told the *Los Angeles Times* reporter, "But it's strange. We've conducted intensive searches in the area after the house had been pelted with stones and we've never come up with anybody who could have thrown them. Reliable witnesses in the neighborhood told us they have seen the stones as they floated down from the sky."

The news article went on to say that the bombardment of the one-story house had begun only after new tenants, W. M. Lowe, his wife, and five children, had moved in the previous July. (It is interesting to note that one of their children was adopted.) Shortly after, Lowe complained about the stone-throwings to the local sheriff's substation. Windows were broken, Lowe's children were slightly bruised, and a deputy's car was once the target of stone-throwings when he arrived to investigate. By Halloween night the family had had enough and moved to another house. New residents moved in shortly after, the news report continued, and they too watched in amazement as the rocks continued to fall.

Even at the outset, the Big Bear case was already showing many of the poltergeist's notorious characteristics. The origin of the rocks, which seemed simply to materialize in mid-air, was never discovered. The stones gently "floated" through the air instead of falling normally, and did not hurt anyone they struck. Also true to form, the stones were usually warm.

Further testimony about the Big Bear case came in the *Los Angeles Times* the next day when the paper printed an interview with one of the present tenants of the house, twenty-year-old Don Beasley. He too told reporters how he had watched the stones drift down on the house. At first he thought that cranks or children were the cause of the nuisance, but abandoned that idea when he actually saw the stones fall straight down from the sky.

"The stones actually seemed to float down. One guy was standing outside and one of the stones hit him on the arm but it didn't hurt him," he told reporters.

At Beasley's request the sheriff returned to investigate the case once more, and again a deputy's car was dented by the large stones that bombarded it.

Many local newspapers had picked up the story by mid-November, and Raymond Bayless, who had read of the case with excited attention, drove to Big Bear on November 11, accompanied by a co-investigator, Mr. Attila von Szalay, in order to interview the witnesses and, with luck, see the rock falls personally. However, it is usually easier to catch witnesses than psychic phenomena, so Bayless began his investigation by questioning all the witnesses to the strange events he could find. Among those interviewed were a local deputy and the present occupants of the house.

The deputy told Bayless and von Szalay that he had been called to the house on five occasions and, although he had seen many stones strike the ground, he had never seen any of them actually fall from the sky. All told, he had seen some twenty stones strike the ground. "I don't think anything human is causing it," he added.

During his interview with Don Beasley and his roommate, the present tenants of the house, Raymond learned that Lowe had warned them that the place was haunted, and that stones had begun falling right on the spot immediately afterward. Two windows and the windshield of a car parked in front of the house were shattered. (The stone-throwings occurred several times a week, and although the attacks were not timed, Raymond estimated that they lasted approximately ten minutes to one-half hour.) Beasley's car had been continually struck by rocks, it seems, and in his notes on the case Raymond made some interesting remarks about the flight of the rocks:

Both Beasley and his roommate said the rocks that had actually been seen striking, or rocks that were known to have just struck, did not seem to have possessed normal velocity, but hit with much less force than expected. They remarked on the fact that the man who was hit was not in the least injured and again they felt that the stone did not display a normal speed of fall.

The rock-throwing, though, had ceased during the previous four days, and it looked to Bayless as though the PK were waning. This decreased his hopes of witnessing the events for himself. But he was at least able to talk with one Big Bear resident who had actually been able to trace the exact trajectory of a rock fall. The witness (left nameless in the Bayless report) had been outside the house at 6:30 one evening when he saw a stone suspended about ten or twelve feet in the air. The grounds were illuminated by house and porch lights. "It coasted down very slow," he told Bayless. The rock had fallen at about a thirty-degree angle and had landed ten feet from him, he claimed. He also said he had picked up rocks that had fallen during earlier bombardments and noticed that they felt hot.

The bombardments tapered off during the Beasley occupancy, so Raymond was too late to see the heavy falls, for by then only isolated stones could be heard now and then thumping onto the vegetation that covered the surrounding area. One evening during his investigation, however, Raymond patrolled the grounds hoping to witness at least one of these incidents. The cold and the dark of the night were trying even for a psychical investigator's patience. Bayless reports in his *The Engima of the Poltergeist*:

At 7:30 P.M. I was startled to hear an object strike the ground about fifteen feet from me. The impact was unmistakable. Unfortunately, in spite of the full, brilliant moon, I simply could not find the missile as it had fallen into a dense clump of weeds that happened to have been in a deep shadow. As a consequence, I cannot actually say that I saw a rock fall, or strike, but taking everything into consideration, the possibility for the unseen object to have been a falling stone is certainly strong.

To his credit, Raymond was the only investigator to uncover the fact that the rock-throwings may not have been the only poltergeist activity at the house. Not mentioned in the sensational newspaper reports, and overshadowed by the police investigations, was the fact that one of the Lowe children had told reporters about hearing somebody walking on the roof of the cabin. Of course, the Lowes dismissed the report at the time, but the rock-throwings began shortly after.

The Big Bear case is almost a textbook example of a stone-throwing poltergeist. However, there is at least one oddity about the Big Bear case that needs explaining: why did the rocks continue to bombard the house *after* the Lowes moved out instead of moving *with* them, as many conventional poltergeists do? This might be explained by a rather recently isolated PK phenomenon which has been called the "linger effect." Parapsychologists have found that the PK force will sometimes "linger on" in the experimental area even after an experiment is over. In the first chapter I discussed the marvelous PK ability of Felicia Parise and mentioned that, even after she had completed a test, her PK would continue infecting the physical area in which the experiment had been run. I would like to explore this a little more thoroughly.

These experiments were carried out by Graham and Anita Watkins at the Foundation for Research on the Nature of Man in Durham. The Watkinses wanted to see if Felicia could exert her PK on a compass by making its needle deflect. She had no difficulty succeeding at this task. Yet, even after the experiment was over, and after she had walked to a far corner of the laboratory, the needle would deflect mysteriously by fifteen degrees when it was replaced in the experimental area. The Watkinses brought both a magnet and a steel blade close to the compass in order to alter the deflection, but the needle was completely unresponsive. Thinking that the compass was malfunctioning, the experimenters removed it from the experimental area, and no sooner were they four feet from the site than the needle returned to normal. When the compass was replaced in the PK area, the needle again deflected and remained unmovable. The Watkinses went back and forth making observations, and found that the PK "sphere of influence" lasted for about twenty-five minutes before dissipating completely.

This experiment excited the Watkinses because they had isolated a similar linger effect during their earlier PK studies on anesthetized mice. During these carefully controlled tests, psychics would try to awaken a particular mouse before a control mouse, both of which had been mildly chloroformed, by projecting some mental force onto it. For each trial, two mice were set side by side and one of them (either the left or the right) would be used for eight consecutive trials. A different pair of mice was used for each trial. A few psychics whom the Watkinses had chosen on the basis of their prior successes on other ESP and PK tests, were remarkably successful at awakening the target mouse. Under normal conditions one would expect the target mice to awaken before the control mice only 50 percent of the time. But during these tests, the target mice were consistently aroused earlier than the control mice. Graham Watkins also discovered a peculiarity in his data. After an experiment was over, when no one was attempting to exert any force over the mice, the mouse on the side used as the target in the previous test *would continue to wake up first* if two of them were placed in the experimental area. This effect again lasted for approximately twenty-five minutes. Once again it would appear that some sort of sphere of influence was being established by the subject while exerting PK and only gradually dissipated. The Watkinses' experiments with Felicia and with the anesthetized mice have given parapsychology its first evidence of an actual PK field.

However, linger effects were known even in the early days of PK testing when subjects were only asked to "will" certain die faces or combinations to roll up more often than could be expected by chance. Two of these investigators, J. G. Pratt in Durham, North Carolina, and Haakon Forwald in Sweden, noted a similar oddity. If they were rolling for a certain number, and were getting good results, this number would still roll up more than chance could account for even *after* they switched to a new target face. Pratt and Forwald believed that this was, in fact, a psychological phenomenon: the inability of the subject to reorient himself to a new target while unconsciously still favoring the old one. Neither experimenter theorized that the results might have been produced by a physical PK effect.

This linger effect may have actually got one investigator into some trouble. It is a famous story reported from the early years of PK testing. A bright new researcher at one parapsychology lab carried out a series of dice-rolls in which he attempted to make 6's come up more often than any other face, and he got very consistent results. Immediately after the test, though, he decided to roll *another* series of throws without attempting to project PK onto them. (This would represent a control series.) The experimenter wanted to prove that if he didn't attempt to influence the dice with PK, the die faces would come up almost evenly, that is, each face occurring once every six throws. But 6's still came up above chance even for this series. The newcomer decided that his dice were biased (loaded) or defective and nullified his experiment. Indeed his dice *could* have been biased; however, he may, in fact, have been confronting the linger effect. Perhaps if he had waited about thirty minutes before going on with his control series his results might have been very different.

In the Big Bear case the PK force may have set up a psychic "field" in order to perpetuate the bombardment. In fact the slow movement of the stones is reminiscent of the way a pebble sinks down through a deep pool of water. The pebble will slowly descend as if "floating." The slow flight trajectory of some poltergeist-thrown stones indicates to me that the rocks are actually moving through a "field" or PK sphere. Perhaps that is why they do not bounce when they strike the ground. (Note how this same phenomenon was reported by Mr. Grotten-dieck, whose testimony opened this chapter.) While some stones may be literally catapulted by PK, others may actually flow through a PK-constructed field similar to the type that Felicia Parise was apparently able to establish.

When the L˙˙es left their house so did the force behind the PK. But the PK *field* may have remained, only to slowly dissipate just as Felicia's PK field did. When you turn off a television set, the screen doesn't instantly go black, it takes a second or so for the residual current to dissipate. The Big Bear case indicates that a similar process might occur during poltergeist outbreaks. If the PK field responsible for the peltings only gradually loses force, we might expect a few more bombardments to occur even after the poltergeist agent has moved away. In many of the cases included in this book, witnesses testified that PK occurrences were still evident after the end of the active poltergeistery. This could be attributed to a similar process at work.

The Big Bear stone-throwing was not the first of its kind that Raymond Bayless and von Szalay had encountered. Almost exactly two years before, a rock-throwing poltergeist had disrupted business at a used-car lot in Lynwood, one of many incorporated cities within the boundaries of the huge Los Angeles megalopolis. Again the first publicity about the case came in the form of a *Los Angeles Times* piece headlined ROCKS PELT USED CAR LOT IN LYNWOOD on September 10, 1960. The story caused the two men to investigate and interview all available witnesses.

According to the lot manager, Claude Mock, the pelting began on September 9 after handyman Anthony Angelo came in for work at 9:30 A.M. The rocks fell all that day and continued over the next two days until

Angelo was arrested by police as a suspect in the mischief. Mock told Bayless that over 200 stones had bombarded the lot during the two-day disturbance and added that the missiles consisted not only of rocks, but of pieces of metal, nuts, and bolts as well. The objects flew in abnormal, unpredictable trajectories, cascading every three minutes or so into the lot from all directions except east and usually moving horizontally. They did not seem to fall from the sky. The stones hit the garage, the office, and often "followed people." The amazed businessman had even seen the rocks strike police officers and handymen as they walked on the lot.

The rock-throwing became so mystifying that at one time thirty police officers were called in to search the neighborhood, but they could find no culprit. Nonetheless they vaguely realized that Angelo was somehow responsible and took the forty-year-old mechanic into custody after one officer claimed he had seen him toss a rock at a car. Significantly the rock falls ceased after Angelo was removed from the premises. Angelo had been hired only two days prior to the outbreak to do odd jobs around the lot, so the manager knew very little about him other than that he seemed disturbed about something.

In order to pursue the case further, since it was obvious that Angelo's absence would also signify the cessation of the bombardment, Raymond interviewed the police captain in charge of the investigation. Even though Angelo was in custody, the captain told Bayless that Angelo could not have caused the bombardment, and admitted that the worker had been under strict police surveillance during times when the rocks showered the lot. He had only arrested Angelo when, observing him through fieldglasses, he had watched him toss a rock at a car. Angelo, when questioned about the incident, denied throwing it. The captain finally had to admit that the case was "not solved."

Other witnesses interviewed described to Raymond the incredible speed of the stones, and how at the height of the disturbance all sorts of objects were hurled about.

In the meantime Attila von Szalay called Angelo's home and spoke to his immigrant mother. Her inability to express herself in English defeated von Szalay's attempt to get any information from her. However, she did manage to tell him that her son had worked at other lots and that "he resents washing cars and working his arms to the bone and gets no money." This statement, of course, might well be the psychological clue to the Lynwood poltergeist.

This rather unsatisfactory interview ended the active investigation of the poltergeist which, due to Angelo's incarceration, had abated only two and a half days after its inception. Nevertheless, the story of the Lynwood poltergeist does not end here, for when Angelo went to trial, the poltergeist went on trial as well in what has to be one of the most bizarre court proceedings in American history.

With Judge Sidney W. Kaufman presiding, a jury trial was held on November 22, 1960. Anthony Angelo, the defendant, was charged with obstructing a police investigation. (Notice that at the trial Angelo was not actually charged with being responsible for the stone-throwings, the paranormal nature of which was to become the focus of the testimony.)

The first witness on the stand was the lot manager, Mr. Mock, who described to the court what he had told

Raymond a month before. During his testimony he added vivid descriptions of the often uncanny flights of the rocks.

"I was in the back office sitting on the corner of a desk looking out the back door," he told the court. "The mechanic came in the door and a rock came in at the same time and went out the front door. It came in a straight line... the first day was the worst. They hit every five or ten minutes."*

Although he was suspicious of Angelo, Mock had not personally seen him throw a rock at a car. (This was the charge that had led to his arrest and was apparently what the trial was all about.)

A recess was called after Mock gave his somewhat lengthy testimony, and at that time Raymond made his first attempt to get a hearing for the poltergeist. After securing the defense attorney's attention, he tried to explain to him the nature of the poltergeist and described the patterns of the stone-slinging poltergeist. Raymond urged the attorney to bring these facts to light, since they might help vindicate Angelo in the eyes of the jury. The lawyer was gruff and rejected the notion. In retrospect, I suppose this was to be expected. After all, in 1960 even fewer people knew about poltergeists than do now, so the attorney probably assumed that Raymond was more of a crank than a genuinely interested party.

As the trial continued, various witnesses testified.

"Were you able to tell where the rocks came from?" asked the examiner as he questioned one police officer.

"No, sir," he answered. "During the two-day span we

---

* The court records have never been published. These quotations are taken from notes made by Raymond Bayless at the trial, which he placed at my disposal.

had as many as thirty officers in the field. We couldn't tell where the rocks came from."

This type of testimony went on for hours. And when the police captain testified, it became more and more uncertain whether Angelo had actually thrown a rock at a car. The captain told the court that he had watched Angelo look about the lot while leaning against a used Nash Rambler. As he continued to watch, he saw Angelo hit the side of the car with his hand two or three times, but admitted that he couldn't tell if anything were actually in the employee's hand. Afterward, testified the captain, Angelo turned and walked away. When the captain returned to the lot he was told that Angelo had been hit by a rock. On inspecting the Rambler, the police found a small dent on it and Angelo was charged with defacing it. Angelo, however, denied ever being near it.

Obviously, the police charge that Angelo had actually been observed throwing a rock at a car was an exaggeration of what had actually taken place. On the other hand, though, the police testimony is typical of the way many skeptical investigators reach to find a normal explanation for the poltergeist no matter how at variance with the facts it is. Angelo probably had lied when he claimed that he had not been near the car. However, it is also likely that he was aware that he was the police's favorite suspect, which may have frightened him into lying.

As the trial went on, the court testimony became rather confusing when Mock, who had at first testified to the mysterious nature of the rock-throwings, began to have second thoughts about his own observations. Now he claimed that since the rocks came when Angelo was hired and stopped when he left, the handyman *must* be responsible. Mock was correct, of course, but he was right for the wrong reasons.

By this time Angelo's attorney began reconsidering Raymond's recommendation that "the poltergeist" should be brought before the court. The proceedings were not going well for Angelo and the attorney knew it. Presenting the idea of the poltergeist might be his final effort to vindicate his client. So, at the next recess, the news that a poltergeist expert was attending the trial was brought to the attention of the judge. Judge Kaufman was more receptive than the attorney had been to the possibility that the rock-throwings were due to a psychic cause. Even though the court was officially in recess, Kaufman availed himself of Raymond's presence and talked to him about the nature and behavior of the poltergeist. As the recess came to an end, Raymond explained to the court that stone-throwing poltergeists were a well-substantiated form of psychic phenomenon and that Angelo therefore had nothing to do (normally, that is) with the stones.

Angelo took the stand after the recess. He denied any culpability in damaging the lot and repeatedly denied that he had thrown any rocks or caused them to fall. Interestingly enough, by this time the issue at stake had veered completely away from whether or not Angelo had interfered with the police investigation as charged. The key point now was: were the rock falls normal or supernormal?

How much Raymond's testimony influenced the court cannot be judged. But Angelo was found "not guilty" after the final arguments were presented. The defense attorney had acceded to Raymond by stating in his final argument that the disturbance must be laid to a "supernatural cause" even though, as emphasized earlier, the actual crime with which Angelo was charged had nothing to do with the nature of the pelting.

The Lynwood poltergeist was not the first of its kind to go to court. All through the strange and at times humorous history of the poltergeist, victims and observers have been ushered into court on all sorts of charges. In 1888 a village-based poltergeist case in Germany landed in court after a small house became the scene of unexplained rock-throwings, banging, and other disturbances. When the flying stones broke a neighbor's windows, the homeowner promptly brought charges against a fifteen-year-old boy named Karl, who he claimed was responsible, and demanded restitution of 12 marks to repair the damage. He was accused of the misdemeanor of counterfeiting the activities of a *Spuk* (ghost).

At the court hearing the boy denied any responsibility for the incidents and stated that he had never thrown or knocked anything. Fourteen witnesses had been brought in to testify. They described the raps heard on the walls of the victimized house, how stones and other projectiles had been thrown about while Karl was under their direct observation. Even the local pastor, Dr. Müller, testified. He stated that as soon as he entered the house he saw a potato fall into a bucket of milk. Thundering poundings on the walls occurred moments later, he added. Then a number of potatoes came flying at his head, one of which struck him.

Unfortunately for Karl, the poltergeist ceased its activity when the boy was taken into custody. Despite the evidence and testimony, the judge drew the only natural conclusion open to him and Karl was given a short jail sentence. The court, the judge added, could only base its conclusions on "enlightened science" and not on tales of ghosts. An appeal was lodged, but rejected.

As the cases above illustrate, stone-throwing poltergeists occur all over the world. In 1964 one such incident occurred in Marilao, Bulacan, in the Philippines. I have nothing on the case other than a news release that appeared in the *Daily Mirror*, a Manila-based paper, on October 26, 1964. It reads:

Who, or what, is the unseen thing that has been throwing stones at whichever house a 14-year-old waif lived in? Ernesto Rabanzos, who has been staying with Ildefonso Santos for two years since the old man's daughter picked him up in Grace Park, is the object of curiosity in this little town that is all a-dither with the stories of how his presence in certain houses has caused stones to rain thereat at night. Among those who have "witnessed" the mysterious stone-throwing are a parish priest, a former councilor, and local residents. According to the stories, since the boy lived with the Santos family in Tabing Ilog, the town, the residence has been the object of stone-throwing seemingly by an invisible intruder. The nuisance got to a point where it prompted Santos to file a criminal action against his neighbors, whom he suspected of malicious mischief. The case was dropped for lack of anybody to accuse. Santos finally turned the boy over to former Councilor Nemesia Santiago, a civic leader. From the day Ernesto moved in, the woman's house was also bombarded with stones. Santiago said she could not accuse the boy of having thrown the stones himself as he was always asleep in the house whenever the strange incidents occurred. The story spread far and wide, and soon the police were called in to guard the former councilor's residence. Still the thing—or the stones—persisted. Finally, the woman consulted the parish priest, who then agreed to take custody of Ernesto. The very day the boy began staying in the convent, church windows and chandeliers were pelted with stones, and at least two persons...were hit. Blessing the church to exorcise evil spirits did no good and the priest gave up his cause as a lost one, and said he would refer the boy to Boys Town in Marinkina, Rezal.

Despite the fact that rock-throwing poltergeists have been frequently reported in the past, there has been a relative dearth of such reports during the last decade. W. G. Roll has failed to uncover even one case during all his years of poltergeist-hunting, and at least one parapsychologist has suggested that the stone-throwing poltergeist might be a thing of the past. However, it may also be that these cases are more rarely reported than conventional poltergeists, since so often the throwings are merely blamed on juvenile pranksters. Nonetheless there is some evidence that stone-throwing cases go on all the time.

For example, a case struck Temple City, California, in June 1977. According to a news story in the June 30 issue of the *Temple City Times*, the rocks had been falling on a small house for several days, breaking windows and striking people standing outside as well. The house was occupied by a couple and their three young children. Neighbors and the local police had scoured the area for the rock-thrower. None was found, even though helicopters had been dispatched to patrol the area.

The case followed a standard pattern. The stone-throwings stopped when the family left the house, but resumed as soon as they returned. The disturbances occurred when the whole family was together, usually commencing in late evening and lasting into the early morning hours. After a few weeks of constant harassment, though, the rock assaults began to ebb and finally dissipated as mysteriously as they had begun.

Unfortunately, by the time Raymond Bayless and I learned of the case, the PK activity had ended. We had missed it by just a few days. We did, however, drive out to take a look at the house. Rocks, some quite large, could be clearly seen covering the roof, but we never witnessed any of the stones in motion.

It is clear that stone-throwing is one of the most common activities of the poltergeist. But there is a more important issue at hand than just substantiating that the poltergeist often engages in this peculiar habit. This is, simply, why does the poltergeist throw stones?

This is a question I cannot easily answer, but one short and practical theory might be that stones are simply the most available missiles. They might be thrown merely because they are handy. However, this idea strikes me as only one possible component of the answer. Stone-throwing poltergeists have been common and have changed so little in their nature over the hundreds of years of recorded poltergeist history, that I believe they are expressing a very definite need of the poltergeist agent. For instance, in the Sanderson case (see p. 139) the poltergeist went to great pains to sort out rocks that had been carefully marked by the witnesses. This was certainly not convenient for the poltergeist and indicates a complex motivation.

The basic purpose of the poltergeist is not to play or create a nuisance; it is to be destructive. Sometimes objects are hurled back and forth until they are deliberately broken. The Seaford poltergeist engaged in this type of specific destructiveness, making this particular trait of the poltergeist seem almost purposeful. Remember, poltergeists can do a tremendous amount of damage. It is my opinion that stones are thrown because they have the potential to do the most damage. Freud has shown that our unconscious mind is a breeding ground for our more fundamental urges and desires. C. G. Jung, Freud's disciple, believed that the unconscious also houses the collective memories of our entire civilization. The poltergeist is the direct expression of our primitive desires to lash out and express hostility, urges that are generally held in check by conscious restraints. Primitive man knew of the destructive power of rocks and from them he fashioned his first weapons and killed his first foes. In biblical times those who broke the law were stoned to death, and this method of punishment is still employed in many primitive cultures. During mob violence stones are the most often and lethally used missiles. When the poltergeist is unleashed, it carries with it the primitive consciousness of humankind. Because it, too, exists to destroy, it employs that most ancient tool of humans— the stone.

Why, then, are people so rarely injured by the poltergeist? This is another question we must confront. People have often been struck by the poltergeist's missiles, and although these objects may strike at high speed, they usually do not cause injury. It is my belief that rocks are thrown to cause physical damage, not to do personal injury. When we are annoyed at someone, more often than not we think of damaging his property rather than doing actual bodily harm to him. This is a more passive means of aggression. Parents often see how, after breaking up a fight between squabbling children, one child will secretly damage the other's toys. The spite becomes focused not at the person directly but indirectly at his belongings. It is more than likely that the poltergeist works along similar psychological lines. These demonstrations are meant to intimidate and nothing more, and thus carefully avoid causing personal injury in most cases.

Even though the poltergeist often refrains from causing personal injury, some poltergeists can become devastatingly harmful ... so destructive and horrifying in fact that even today we must wonder if these outbreaks are due solely to the PK projections of an individual, or to some outside and evil force or entity.

5

Bizarre Poltergeists

"It's really a mystery and if it's not a chemical reaction or spontaneous combustion, then I don't know what it can be," complained Captain S. H. Joiner, fire chief of Talladega, Alabama, to a newsman.

Joiner was referring to an epidemic of fires plaguing the family of thirty-two-year-old Calvin Tuck, whose cabin had caught fire on twenty-two occasions over the past few days. Just the day before—August 28, 1959—seventeen fires had broken out, he told reporters. Tuck, his wife, and their six children (aged six months to nine years) had been literally burned out of their house and, bemoaned Joiner, the fire department was at a complete loss either to explain or to prevent the blazes. The fires seemed to ignite from the ceiling, and on some occasions flammable items spontaneously burst into flames. Even nonignitable objects were consumed in the mysterious fires that broke out every fifteen minutes or so during the height of the disturbances. There was no frayed or exposed wiring in the house, and the flames resembled those of chemical fires, he added.

The horror had apparently begun on the morning of August 25, when three fires broke out in the house. At first the Tucks didn't realize that anything supernatural was afflicting them. Nonetheless, the same bizarre phenomena began again the next day. So, in absolute despair, the Tucks called in the fire department, since they were concerned that they would eventually be unable to control the small blazes themselves. Newspaper reporters were quick to the scene as well. But no one realized that these small fires heralded the onset of one of the most bizarre poltergeist outbreaks ever recorded.

Tuck could only conclude that the fires were being started by some electrical malfunction in the house, which he had been unable to detect. Chemicals, freak electrical sparks, and electrostatic causes had all been considered as he searched for the cause of the fires, but were all discarded as unlikely possibilities. Soon he realized that there was something unnatural about them. Being somewhat superstitious, he was unable to overcome the feeling that the house was hexed, and he moved into another home after packing up his belongings. For some reason, however, before leaving he piled all his family's clothes, mattresses, and other possessions in front of the house and burned them himself. (While I do not know the reason for this, Tuck may have based his actions on a local superstition.) The Tucks moved into a second home, but the fires continued to plague them there; five unexplained blazes broke out on the first day of their occupancy. The next day offered no relief, and once again fire officials were called in by the family.

When investigator R. E. Hogan arrived at the Tuck home with two police officers, he could only describe the house and yard as "if a tornado had ripped into it." Clothes and furniture were scattered everywhere. Tuck was not at home at the time, but another fire erupted as soon as the men arrived; this time a quilt hanging on a tree in the yard suddenly burst into flames. Lieutenant Cooley, one of the police officers who had accompanied Hogan, ripped it from the tree and tried to light the remains with a match. Although it smoldered, it would not ignite into flames. Later, just after the police left, a loaf of bread burst into flames.

Because of all the publicity and commotion the mysterious fires were stirring in the local community, the residents looked upon Tuck with some suspicion. They believed he was cursed and they certainly didn't want him in *their* town. Even his landlord, who was also his brother-in-law, succumbed to fear of the supernatural and evicted the family from the house before it was gutted completely. So, once more, Tuck and his family had to move. Luckily, his father was more sympathetic and invited them to stay with him. The Tucks moved in on September 2, their third home in just over a week. Meanwhile, in order to prevent further fires, Tuck consulted a local "witch" who gave him a spell to rid him of an alleged "Voodoo hex" which had been laid upon him. Unfortunately the spell didn't work. After only a few days of peace, seven fires broke out in the elder Tuck's house.

By this time, both police and fire officials were actively investigating the case. However, police investigators were not as interested in finding some freak explanation for the fires as were the fire inspectors. Chief of Police Leon Curlee was not as prone to believe in the supernatural as were the Tucks. He suspected arson. He believed that the fires were caused by combustible chemicals and desired nothing less than to catch the arsonist. Despite his vigil, though, unexplained fires continued to break out throughout the day of his investigation. Consequently Tuck moved once more to a home in a neighboring town and the police and fire investigators followed. But this move did nothing to counter the fire plague. Totally at a loss to handle the situation, the police finally placed Calvin Tuck under a sort of "protective custody" but released him soon after, still having shed no light on the fire mystery.

All during this curious affair several fire inspectors repeatedly maintained that the fires were due to arson. Nonetheless the burned remnants of household items failed to show any telltale signs such as chemical residue. The fire officials were ready to abandon the case by this time, but the police were determined to explain the fires, and the case came to a quick conclusion when they reported that nine-year-old Calvin Tuck, Jr. had confessed to setting them. He had started them all, they said, by striking matches. The youngster even began to boast about having set the fires, and his motive, he said, was to get the family to move back to Birmingham.

This confession, however, sheds practically no light on the fires. In fact, all it accomplished was to give the fire department a good excuse to withdraw from the case. Calvin Jr.'s confession is similar to ones made in many poltergeist cases. As I mentioned earlier, it is not odd for the probable agent to "confess" that he or she produced phenomena which he or she could not possibly have committed. Judge Hurst, who presided over a hearing in which formal charges were lodged against Calvin, released the boy on the grounds that insufficient evidence existed to warrant juvenile authority action. (Only later did it come out that the boy was badgered into the confession by police officials.) Even Fire Marshal Frank Caven did not believe the admission; he pointed out to investigators that the color of the flames did not indicate that they had been set by matches. Normally noncombustible wallpaper was seen to burn and the fires often started high up on the walls or ceiling out of the reach of a young child.

The "Voodoo Fires of Alabama," as this case has been dubbed, is a superb example of one of the most unusual of all poltergeists, the fire poltergeist. In one respect, fire poltergeists are similar to stone-throwers. They usually concentrate their force solely toward producing one type of nuisance, in this case starting fires. These two types of poltergeist activity may often occur simultaneously. During the West Indies stone-throwing poltergeist attack recounted earlier, the victimized house caught fire and was gutted at the end of the outbreak. As with stone-throwings, at times mysterious fire represents only one element of a more conventional poltergeist. In other cases, fires are the poltergeist's only or primary method of disruption.

But how do we really know that the Alabama case was a true poltergeist? After all, it certainly didn't behave like a conventional one. It didn't throw stones, move furniture about, or produce loud noises. Nonetheless the Alabama case does resemble conventional poltergeist cases in other ways. First, the fires followed the family as they sought refuge in several different homes. Conventional poltergeists also show this peculiar mobility. Second, the fire rampage lasted only a few weeks and then ceased. This is well within the "normal" time span of a typical poltergeist. Finally, young Calvin's behavior (that is, confessing to the phenomena) is a typical "poltergeist reaction."

Fire poltergeists represent yet another dimension of the poltergeist, and they have been recorded throughout the poltergeist's unpopular history. For instance, a complex poltergeist case which involved fire-igniting was reported from India in 1920. The chief witness was A. S. T. Pillay, a local magistrate in the Tanjore district. He was a Catholic convert and did not write his account for publication, but only did so at the request of private church and local officials who wished to have documentation pertaining to the phenomena on file. The poltergeist, which lasted only two weeks, first broke out in Pillay's house on March 3:

The clothes in the upstairs which were left [on] the "rope" took fire and the clothes were burning, [recalled Pillay in his written deposition.] Females became aware of the fire as soon as the child lying in the cradle upstairs having been terrified on seeing the fire, cried out. The fires were extinguished by water and the wet half-burnt clothes placed on the chair. Half an hour after when the females went to upstairs again the wet clothes and the chair were burning. Thinking that the fire was due to some carelessness of my daughter who had an occasion to light a chimney—upstairs, she was given a good beating.

The next day two more fires ignited in the house and more conventional poltergeist activity was observed. Pictures of Catholic saints were thrown down from walls, glass shattered, and cow dung smeared over the walls. Like many poltergeists, this one was apparently antireligious in nature.*

During his ordeal with the poltergeist, Pillay noted

*Many cases have been cited in previous chapters in which clergymen were attacked upon entering a poltergeist-affiliated house. Likewise, poltergeists will often isolate religious items for specific acts of violence. It is not odd to read that Bibles, icons, or religious paintings are often molested by the poltergeist; and it is no wonder, then, that so many accused the devil of propagating these attacks.

that pictures of saints were specifically thrown about and defiled; crosses drawn in chalk on the house were rubbed with cow dung; and religious objects were apported. As Pillay testified in his account:

> ... I took a standing crucifix of black wood and placed it on the [mantle piece] by the side of the hearth. I myself sat about three feet to the north and was reciting the Apostles' Creed over and over. Within a second the crucifix was missing. To my great grief and extreme sorrow I found the crucifix in the fire and the wood was burning. None else was there except me.

During another series of incidents, a crucifix disappeared from the house only to be found later on the roof. As if to mock Pillay's religious observances, crosses were drawn in cow dung on the walls in sealed-off rooms, while religious objects placed or hung in the house to ward off the "demon" would vanish almost as soon as they had been positioned. In addition, objects were continually thrown at the family members as they sat down to their meals.

With no other solution in sight, Pillay moved his family to a new house. This, of course, changed nothing, and the poltergeist announced its continuing presence soon after the move by igniting two brooms. Again religious medallions were displayed to ward off the evil, and once more they disappeared. The poltergeist also engaged in invisible struggles with the family. Once Pillay watched in horror as it tried to pull a cooking vessel from the hands of his son-in-law. A tug of war ensued between the young man and the invisible force as it tried to tear the pot from his hands. This seemed to enrage the poltergeist, and soon bricks, bowls, and every throwable object imaginable were hurled at the family.

Some of the fires were psychically ignited by the poltergeist. Sometimes the poltergeist would transport already burning objects through the house, setting additional fires as it traveled.

Pillay describes several of these fires in his account. One evening he came home to find the hallway of the house damp with water. His frightened family told him that firewood from the hearth had been thrown into the hall, causing an instant blaze. By this time Pillay had had enough, and he openly challenged "the devil," condemning it back to hell and offering prayer:

After finishing it [the Apostles' Creed], I went to the middle hall and went towards the eastern room about ten feet off the hearth, with my boy aged two in one of my hands. He was also walking with me. The devil suddenly took another big piece of burning fire and threw it with great force between my legs. I at once turned back and saw the whole hall filled with fire.

Soon after this incident something else occurred that may help us to understand this poltergeist. Ominous writing was found on a wall exhorting Pillay to return to his Hindu faith. It therefore seems likely that Pillay may have been undergoing intense inner conflict and guilt over his conversion to Christianity. Since he was undoubtedly still steeped in Indian culture and religion, he may have engendered the poltergeist as an expression of the deep-seated guilt resulting from his conversion. In this light it is no wonder that the poltergeist initiated such assaults against religious objects placed in the house. Significantly enough the attacks ended after several exorcisms had been conducted in the house.

The one outstanding feature of the fire poltergeist is its persistence. It seems that the fires are usually not ignited merely to annoy the family, but are set over and over again purposefully until a house is finally burned down. For example, a news item in the April 7, 1947, issue of *Time* magazine reported:

In Woodstock, Vt. a fire broke out in the basement of the Wendell Walker home on Sunday; the staircase caught fire on Monday; an upstairs partition blazed on Tuesday; the jittery Walkers moved out on Wednesday; the house burned down on Thursday.

This brief notice sums up the persistence of the fire poltergeist quite well.

Vincent Gaddis, a well-known writer on psychic subjects, also used this news item to open a discussion on fire poltergeists, which he included in his excellent book *Mysterious Fires and Lights*. Although not a professional parapsychologist, Gaddis is probably the only modern authority on the paranormal who has tried to determine just what process is at work during these outbreaks. As an ex-newspaper reporter he has collected many accounts of fire-poltergeist incidents that have been reported in the news media over the years. Some of his cases, which he has drawn from news dispatches, clearly illustrate the ferocity of the fire poltergeist:

In April 1941 a fire poltergeist broke out in the home of William Hackler of Odon, Indiana. Between the hours of 8 and 11 A.M. nine fires ignited in different parts of the unwired house. A calendar on the wall caught fire, a pair of overalls hanging over a door burst into flame, and the *inside* of a book was found burning. All told, twenty-eight fires eventually plagued the family. A week later, Hackler tore the house down and built a new one.

In January 1958 Mrs. Charles King of Glendive,

Montana, and her two teen-age daughters were afflicted by a fire poltergeist. Fire inspectors removed all household combustible items, yet during the next seven days several fires terrified the family. They ceased as suddenly and mysteriously as they had begun.

An unusual fire poltergeist focused on the Williamson family in Bladenboro, North Carolina, in 1932. Household objects would burst into flame, but nearby, flammable materials were never so much as singed. On one occasion, a dress Mrs. Williamson was wearing ignited, but she was not burned. Two members of the family ripped the dress from the frightened woman, but neither was burned. Representatives from the gas company and the electric company, as well as fire-control experts, all visited the house but could offer no solution for the incidents.

We could cite an endless list of such cases and, as Vincent Gaddis sadly concludes, "We could go on and on with cases of this type.... Moreover in this troubled world, they seem to be increasing. I have collected more cases in the past ten years than in the preceding twenty."

According to Gaddis, the most amazing fire poltergeist ever recorded was the 1948 Macomb, Illinois, case. The Willey family farm, where Willey lived with his wife, his brother-in-law, and his two children, was the scene of the attack. Day after day brown spots appeared on the wallpaper of the five-room house, and visitors testified that these spots reached an estimated temperature of 450 degrees Fahrenheit. They would then burst into flames. In an abortive attempt to help the Willeys, friends and neighbors stationed themselves all over the house with buckets of water in hand to drench the spots as they formed. No one could explain the fires. Fire chief Fred Wilson even told reporters that "... the whole thing is so screwy and fantastic that I'm almost ashamed to talk about it."

Not only did the brown spots appear on the wallpaper, but during the following week they began to form on the porch, on curtains, and eventually on almost any combustible material in the house. As news of the fires spread the farm was overrun with curiosity-seekers and self-appointed investigators. Air Force representatives were sure that either high-frequency radio waves or bizarre radioactivity effects were the cause of the fires. Lewis Gust, an Air Force technician and spokesman who took an interest in the case, noted how extremely short radio waves could set off flash bulbs in flying planes and felt a similar phenomenon was causing the Willeys' problems. Another expert disagreed. He argued that, since no other fire incidents had been reported from neighboring farms, Gust's theory was inadequate to explain the blazes.

Arson investigators were the next "experts" who tried to determine the nature of the fires. They theorized that the fires were being caused by combustible gases accumulating in the walls of the farmhouse. But this theory didn't explain the facts either. Consequently, in a final attempt to resolve the case, they badgered a "confession" from Willey's niece, Wanet. As Gaddis humorously comments about this confession, Wanet must have had "...incredible persistence, an unlimited supply of matches, and blessed with exceptionally nearsighted relatives and neighbors."

Nonetheless, young Wanet probably was at least the supernormal cause of the fires. She was extremely unhappy. She wanted to live with her mother, and not with her father, to whom she had been awarded after her parents' divorce. Just as with many other children, the desire to live elsewhere had ignited the poltergeist. One sees in Wanet a similarity to Virginia Campbell.

But what about the actual mechanics of the fire poltergeist? How does it manipulate the blazes or ignite them? Few parapsychologists have tried to answer these questions. However, Gaddis has offered us one tentative theory about the cause of fire-igniting poltergeists, which is based on the supposition that the poltergeist is a psychological mechanism used to deal with frustration, hate, and repression. In this respect his ideas are virtually the same as Fodor's and Roll's. As in most conventional cases, he argues, fire poltergeists often focus on a disturbed child. From this observation he suggests that the fire poltergeist might be a product of PK-induced electrical effects, in other words, PK having a penchant for, or focusing on, manipulation of sources of electrical energy. He writes in *Mysterious Fires and Lights:*

There is a definite relationship between electrical phenomena and mediumship plus psychical phenomena in general. Accounts of luminous appearances and lights, ranging from pin-points to globular forms a foot or so in diameter, have appeared in séance reports. During periods of other phenomena there have been changes in the intensity of electrical currents in buildings. Mary Roberts Rinehart, the novelist, in her autobiography, tells of lights being mysteriously turned on and off in her home. Harry Price . . . tells of a young nursemaid whose poltergeist manifestations consisted of turning on every electrical appliance and lamp in the house while she was sleeping. . . .

Gaddis believes that somehow the poltergeist agent projects minute amounts of electrical energy normally stored in the body, which then produces or manipulates elecrical forces to cause the fires. These PK "sparks" then ignite objects into flames.

However, this theory cannot explain why normally noncombustible objects are also consumed by the fire poltergeist. This fact has led expert A. R. G. Owen to suggest in his book *Can We Explain the Poltergeist?*:

> If we admit that forces exist which vibrate solids so that they produce sounds, then it is hard to see any limitations set in principle upon the effects that can be produced. In principle the natural molecular agitation of a solid body could be so speeded up that the body becomes hot and eventually bursts into flames.

Because they are rare today, few fire poltergeists have been investigated by contemporary parapsychologists. They appear to be even rarer than stone-throwers or object-hurlers, so we simply do not have the type of detailed data on them that we possess on more conventional cases. This state of affairs may be changing, however, for after years of poltergeist-chasing, William Roll and his associate Gerald Solfvin recently analyzed a fire poltergeist that erupted in Michigan in 1974.

The phenomena began disturbing the lives of the middle-class family in July (the names of the family and the city were withheld from publication) and at first consisted solely of poundings and explosions. The noises occurred only at night in rapid outbursts of knocks and, after a lull, resumed *every night* for several days and seemed to focus on a twenty-one-year-old epileptic son. The poltergeistery abated when the son, Peter, entered a hospital, but returned after his release, so there can be little doubt that his presence was instrumental to the PK.

However, after his release from the hospital, the poundings began to break out during the day as well. By November the raps had intensified so greatly that onlookers compared them to the sounds produced by TNT detonations. These explosions caused the breakage of china and produced a ten-foot crack in the ceiling. The explosions were heard even when Peter was under close surveillance. In December object-throwings occurred for the first time.

Unfortunately Roll and Solfvin did not witness any of the rappings or object-throwings themselves, since these events had abated by the time they were called in to investigate. However, when they began their investigation in February 1975, the fire-raising was imminent. Three fires eventually broke out, the third one damaging a bathroom and two bedrooms. Roll's only conclusion about the case was that the poltergeist may have been linked to Peter's epilepsy, since in recent years a number of cases centering on epileptic agents had been reported.

Fire-raising is only one bizarre behavior of the poltergeist. Another even rarer form is the "biting poltergeist." The Eleanore Zugun case, in which the girl was bitten and lacerated with welts, is a typical example of this phenomenon. Nonetheless, her wounds may have been due to psychological factors. For example, a hypnotic subject will produce a blister on his arm if he is told that a pencil held to it is really a lighted cigarette. Eleanore's bites may have been caused by a similar form of unconscious autosuggestion. However, in other cases, the bites seem paranormally produced. However, very few biting poltergeists have been reported in recent years. There was one case, though, in Indianapolis, Indiana, in 1962 that W. G. Roll was able to study. The victimized house was inhabited by Mrs. Renata Beck, her immigrant mother, Mrs. Lina Gemmecke, and her thirteeen-year-old daughter, Linda.

The poltergeist appeared for the first time on March 10. This was, coincidentally, the birthdate of Mrs. Beck's father from whom she had not heard in twenty years. Small objects began to fly throughout the house, smashing on impact. No sooner had the PK started than puncture marks appeared on Mrs. Beck's arms. Moments later, Mrs. Gemmecke cried out; she too had been "stung" five or six times. All told, Mrs. Gemmecke was bitten on fourteen separate occasions, the number of punctures varying with each attack. Even Roll witnessed this odd phenomenon on the first day of his visit to the Beck household:

> On the evening of the day I came, Mrs. Beck and I were discussing the disturbances in the kitchen. Mrs. Gemmecke, who was alone in her room, called out. When we rushed in, we found one puncture mark on her upper right arm. Ten minutes later, when we were back in the kitchen, she again cried out. When I came into her room, I found her clutching her arm over the sleeve. I rolled the sleeve up and saw four puncture marks, from two of which blood was flowing. Two days later, also in the evening, she received three more punctures, this time on her right breast.

Although Mrs. Gemmecke tried to convince Roll (and herself) that the bites were caused by insects or spiders, Roll once observed her holding a cross to the punctures, certainly indicating that the woman attributed them to quite a different assailant. The only family member not persecuted by the poltergeist was thirteen-year-old Linda. In fact, the elder women were often bitten when

Linda was away. And, although Mrs. Beck was attacked, Mrs. Gemmecke was the prime victim. Roll did not think any skin condition was responsible for the wounds, since the bites often bled. On March 18 the bitings stopped, heralding the onset of a new form of harassment. Now rappings broke out over the house.

This change of focus is commonly reported in many cases, and as I have suggested before, poltergeist infestations seem more like motivated attacks than random disturbances. Stone-throwings and fire-setting are all specific attack strategies. In the Indianapolis case, the strategy was biting. Yet later on the poltergeist willingly and apparently intelligently changed its battle plan. This is the very type of intelligent, motivated act which would indicate that the PK is, in fact, caused by an agency independent of the family, and is an aspect of the poltergeist that many parapsychologists have overlooked. The Indianapolis poltergeist did not *merely* stop biting Mrs. Gemmecke; it stopped in order to reorganize its force into a new maneuver. This action reveals a level of intelligence that leads me to believe that some poltergeists may actually develop an independent will of their own. This is a theory that researchers such as W. G. Roll have constantly played down in their discussions on the phenomenon.

Roll was still in Indianapolis and on hand when the raps began. He reported that they sounded like someone knocking on doors and walls. However, he could not pin down the specific source of the raps and often found himself rushing up and down the stairway in pursuit of the poltergeist. It was impossible for one person to study the phenomena adequately, so Roll was joined by a co-worker, Dr. David Blumenthal, a clinical psychologist from Indianapolis who had collaborated with Roll on an earlier case. With his aid, Roll monitored the whole house and the family members, and verified that no one was faking the disturbances.

Even though the knockings were as persistent as the bitings, typical object-throwings were the most dramatic PK displays in the case. As Roll reports in his book *The Poltergeist*:

Suddenly a small glass vase from the kitchen table flew through the open door and fell to the rug by my feet. The vase did not break; nevertheless there was a loud explosive sound. I was facing Mrs. Beck but not looking directly at her. It was possible, therefore, that she might have thrown the vase. However, this would not explain the sound, which was as loud as a pistol shot. I at once examined the vase. There was no sign of foreign substances on it or on the floor. Unusually loud sounds are often reported in connection with poltergeist incidents.

Finally the poltergeist activity became too unnerving for the two older women. They became overwrought at the slightest provocation. A police investigator saw Mrs. Gemmecke screaming and throwing things during one of these hysterical fits at the height of the rampage and promptly arrested her for being the perpetrator of the disturbances. With the police and court pressuring her, the poor woman decided to return to Germany. Perhaps this is ironic, for during the plague Mrs. Gemmecke had cried out, "Ist Amerika verhekst? So war es nie in Deutschland!" (Is America bewitched? It was never like this in Germany!)

In his technical and clinical analysis of the Indianapolis case, which was published in the January 1970 issue of the *Journal of the American Society for Psychical Research*, Roll suggests that although a teen-ager was conspicuously present in the house, there was little to indicate that she was the prime factor in the outbreak. Instead he found signs of intense strain between Mrs. Beck and her mother. The younger woman was often vocally critical of her mother and considered her to blame for her parents' divorce. She also felt that her mother was a drain on her finances. Although a clinical psychologist in fact did find that Linda was harboring the type of hostility often associated with poltergeist agents, her hostility was not repressed. This is not typical of most poltergeist children. Mrs. Gemmecke, on the other hand, showed more signs of instability than did the others. She suffered from depression, overused psychological defense-mechanisms, and tried to put up what Roll described as a "good front." Deeper analysis showed that the woman endured feelings of inadequacy and rejection, was coping with sexual adjustment problems, and was hostile toward her daughter.

Roll concludes his report on the Indianapolis case with the query, "Poltergeist für zwei?" Departing from his usual theories about the poltergeist, Roll argues that the teen-age daughter was *not* the instigator of the poltergeist but that *both* of the older women generated it as an outgrowth of their interpersonal conflicts.

Even though Roll could never isolate the cause of the poltergeist, the Indianapolis case does tell us a great deal about the nature of biting poltergeists. The fact that two people were bitten, one to the point of bleeding, suggests that the wounds were not psychosomatically induced, but were actually inflicted by PK.

Although biting poltergeists are rare in this century,

they can be especially vicious. Perhaps the most famous and demonic of all biting cases on record was the Bristol poltergeist of 1761-1762.

Although many people witnessed the Bristol poltergeist, our best source of information about it is a booklet written by a Mr. Henry Durbin, which was published posthumously. Durbin had heard of the case through news reports and spent several days at the Giles home making detailed records of what he observed.

Like so many poltergeists, this one announced its presence by first producing scratching sounds on the bedposts of Molly and Dobby Giles. Shortly after, the scratching sounds escalated to raps. Mr. Giles was the first to see the PK at work. As he watched the children in their room in the hope of catching a mischievous servant making the noises, he saw a box cover move by itself. Afterward his daughters' clothes were dumped out of a box onto the floor. Giles took Molly with him to another room but no sooner had she been put to bed than she cried out that her feet were being pinched.

Full-scale PK intensified the plague. Durbin once watched as a wine glass floated upward from its place on a chest, moved slightly backward, and then quickly propelled itself at a nurse staying in the house. It struck her a hard blow. It looked exactly as if an invisible hand had actually thrown it. The object lifted itself up as though grasped, moved slowly backward in a wind-up motion before the throw, and was flung quickly forward.

Durbin also witnessed the bitings and woundings. As he records in his written account on the case:

There was a loud knocking against the table and I saw a chair move in which Molly sat so as almost to throw her down.

Dobby cried the hand was about her sister's throat [the children often reported seeing ghostly hands] and I saw the flesh at the side of her throat pushed in, whiten as if done with fingers, though I saw none.

These woundings did not seem to be psychosomatic in nature. Sometimes they were accompanied by even more unnatural effects, which cannot easily be explained by any psychological cause. Durbin reported:

... seven of us being there in the room, four days later: Molly said she was bit in the arm, and presently Dobby cried out the same. We saw their arms bitten about twenty times that evening. Their arms were put out of bed, and they lay on their backs. They could not do it themselves, as we were looking at them the whole time. We examined the bites and found on them the impression of eighteen or twenty teeth, with saliva or spittle all over them in the shape of a mouth, almost all of them very wet, and the spittle smoking [*sic*], as if just spit out of the mouth. I took up some of it on my finger to try the consistency of it, and Mr. ———— did the same, and we found it clammy like spittle, and it smelt rank.

Sometimes spittle was seen to fall on Molly as though from the ceiling.

The bitings continued for the duration of the case and eventually the children received cuts as well. In fact during one attack Molly was cut to the point of bleeding some forty times. By February, two months after the onset of the poltergeist, the phenomena became more violent and the children were literally thrown out of bed even when visitors tried to hold them down. Several of the witnesses, including Durbin, could even feel invisible hands restraining them, or would see hand marks appear on the children at these times. The children were also occasionally pulled by their necks and dragged about their bedroom.

With no other hope in sight, the clergy were finally brought in to investigate. When they asked the "entity" questions in Latin and Greek the "scratchings" answered correctly via a code. Unfortunately, since Durbin made his exit before the end of the case, we really do not know the outcome of this nearly demonic poltergeist.

Fire-raising and biting are two ways by which the poltergeist can attack. A third way is by water precipitation. Watery poltergeists, which cause jets of water to form or pop from walls and ceilings of the victimized house, are perhaps the rarest type of all bizarre poltergeists. Water precipitation will sometimes accompany more conventional poltergeistery, while at other times it will be the sole means of disruption.

There are very few cases of water poltergeists on record. However, this type—like fire and biting poltergeists—also seems to employ a specific and purposeful attack strategy. Biting is a strategy the poltergeist uses to attack and persecute its victim directly. Fire seems to be the strategy it uses to drive people from their homes. Although water poltergeists are usually milder than either the biting or fire-igniting poltergeists, they do seem to attack in order to cause material damage, and never seem to do personal harm. One of the few historical accounts that has come down to us reports how the home of a public prosecutor, M. Marracino, was thrown into disorder in Ancona, Italy, in 1903 by a water poltergeist. During the case both he and his two sons were deluged by mysterious jets of water.

Hats were filled with it, their beds were flooded, and all sorts of liquids—milk, wine, coffee—were spilled continually over the floor. The events were linked to Marracino's young daughter.

One of the few investigated and well-authenticated modern cases of a watery poltergeist occurred in Methuen, Massachusetts, in 1963. The case was followed up by Raymond Bayless who, as usual, kindly placed his extensive file on the case at my disposal.

The poltergeist first caught public attention when the *Lawrence Eagle-Tribune* reported that a mysterious water plague was following the Francis Martin family from house to house. The story went on to say that in October the family had noticed a wet spot on the wall of their TV room. No sooner had the spot appeared than a loud "pop" resounded and water jetted from the wall. This activity continued for several days until there was so much water in the house that the Martins and their daughter had to seek refuge in a relative's apartment in nearby Lawrence.

As might be expected, their flight was useless. The water-poppings continued at Martin's mother-in-law's home to the consternation of the deputy fire chief who had been called in to investigate. In fact five rooms had been drenched by the time the fire authorities arrived. There was little they could do, other than check over the house for leaks. Needless to say, they found none. One official, Deputy Mains, actually saw a spray of water break through a plaster wall and jet two feet out into the room. Although he would not believe that anything supernatural was going on, he did note that odd popping sounds always preceded the incidents. No other apartment in the building reported anything unusual.

Since the Martins could find no peace away from home, they returned to Methuen. Even more bizarre activity occurred upon their return. Not only did water continue to precipitate, but the humidity inside the house fluctuated wildly. Finally someone turned off the water supply and the pipes were drained. But that did not stem the flooding and the water just kept coming. The Martins could find no relief. After the house became intolerably wet once again they moved back to their relative's apartment... and the water problem went right along with them.

When Raymond Bayless learned about the case, he immediately began to look for witnesses who had been at the house and found one man who had actually seen the watery goings-on. He told Bayless in a letter that he had been in the house at the time of the incident when suddenly Martin's daughter called out from the kitchen, "There's the water again!" Running to the kitchen the witness saw water coming out of the wall. But, he wrote, he didn't believe the girl faked the water disturbances since they also occurred in her absence.

Mrs. Martin also corresponded with Bayless: "The water jets out for about 20 seconds and then there will be a 15 minute interval and it starts someplace else," she wrote. "There's a little tremor and then a 'whoosh' and then the water."

The phenomena gradually petered out, and the case was never solved.

Another water-poltergeist case I know of must rank as one of the strangest on record, though it has never been published or even officially reported.

The phenomenon plagued a family (name withheld) in the midwest. For identification purposes I'll place the case in Minnesota. In this case there was a disturbed adolescent on hand, but also a chronically disturbed family situation as well. Although the family's teen-age son was the focus of the PK, the parents were just as much to blame for the PK that was afflicting them. They were abnormally possessive of their son, who had never been allowed to attend school. Obviously it was a rather unfortunate family situation, and they were undergoing professional counseling during the poltergeist manifestations, which had lasted for several years. Raps sounded on the walls, objects tipped over, and pools of water appeared mysteriously all over the house.

The most amazing aspect of the Minnesota case is that the poltergeist seemed to attack investigators and onlookers as well. The Psychical Research Foundation (PRF) sent an investigator to look into the case during the late 1960s. He witnessed the poltergeist, but had a peculiar reaction to it. Although he was an experienced investigator, he became unusually frightened by this case. After he returned home he abandoned parapsychology entirely, feeling that poltergeists were not something to play with. One of the deciding factors in his decision was that the phenomena—lights turning on and off by themselves, mysterious pools of water, and so forth—started occurring in his own home. In other words, the poltergeist had apparently followed him back to Durham.

Dr. John Artley, who is now a faculty member in the Department of Electrical Engineering at Duke University, was the second investigator sent by the Psychical Research Foundation to Minnesota. However, he witnessed only two incidents. While sitting in the house one evening, he saw several figurines rattle on a stand,

and later a loud blow resounded from the wall in front of him as he lay in bed.

There were other peculiarities about the case as well. The family had kept detailed notes on the poltergeist, which they parceled together and gave to him. This packet became somewhat of a "cursed" object because the poltergeist followed wherever it went. Artley at one point placed the notes in the glove compartment of his car. Several days later, after he had almost forgotten about them, he returned to his car after having run an errand, and found the notes scattered all over the front seat. Admittedly the car was not locked, so the notes could have been tossed about by vandals. But the strange thing was that the notes were *wet* and an envelope was found on the floor of the car resting in a little pool of liquid.

When I asked Dr. Artley about the case he told me that a psychiatrist helping the family work out their difficulties once took possession of the notes, and that same night his two children complained that they heard knocking noises from the attic as they tried to sleep.

Humans weren't the only ones to have their difficulties with the notes, which were later used for some unusual animal experiments. In 1975 Dr. Robert Morris, an animal behaviorist and now a lecturer in parapsychology at the University of California, Santa Barbara, who was in Durham at the time, told me about two mini-experiments the PRF staff carried out with the notes. In one test the packet was dropped into a cage full of gerbils. The animals responded by kicking shavings from their cage over it as though trying to bury it. A normal packet placed in the cage did not provoke any response from the animals, but then neither did the poltergeist package when it was reintroduced later. In another experiment the packet was placed before a rattlesnake and the reptile immediately assumed an attack position. A control package elicited no response at all.

These tests, intriguing as they are, are not proof of anything, however. The PRF researchers could not rule out the possibility that the animals were reacting to some odor on the packet, which was imperceptible to less sensitive noses. It could also be that they had "cued" the animals by dropping the packet in front of them too quickly, thus causing alarm.

Water, fire, and biting are all persecutions used by the poltergeist. They seem more like attack strategies than psychic manifestations, and this very fact may be telling us a great deal about the poltergeist. In analyzing the cases recounted in this chapter, one can see that as the poltergeist grows in intensity it reveals two traits. First, the disturbance will often become more intelligently managed. Second, the outbreaks eventually take on the form of a full-scale attack. They are intelligently planned and executed, and will even change strategies. The point I am trying to make is simply this: as the poltergeist grows more and more powerful, and expands its repertoire of aggravations, the more it looks as if we are dealing with an actual disembodied entity or being who is directing the operation.

The idea that poltergeist outbreaks represent a planned attack is not better illustrated than in a very recent case that has become known as "The Devil in Daly City." This unusual case illustrates just how nefarious the poltergeist can be.

The Daly City, California, poltergeist, which began in

1972, focused on a young couple, Jan and Brian Neven (pseudonyms used in the reports) and their newly born baby. Spontaneous fires broke out in their home, house guests were punched by invisible blows and even hurled to the ground. Objects were overturned or disappeared only to materialize later. San Francisco psychologist Freda Morris was called to investigate and counsel the family while the case was still active and was a witness to the strange ordeal. Her detailed reports, published in the July and August 1974 issues of *Fate* magazine, constitute the fullest description of the case on record.

The poltergeist had begun two months before Dr. Morris was called in and had followed the Nevens as they fled to three different homes and to a motel. Brian Neven, aged twenty-seven, was an Orthodox Jew married to a Catholic and had converted to his wife's religion during the outbreak. As will be seen, this religious conflict between the Nevens may have had an important bearing on the poltergeist.

The Nevens told Dr. Morris that the poltergeist had begun its haunt shortly after little Stephen's birth, when doors started unlocking and opening by themselves. Brian was unable to catch any prowler, and disembodied voices and eerie apparitions broke out soon after.

The poltergeist did not abate when Dr. Morris began her investigation, and it continued to upset pieces of furniture and other objects during her stay—although always in the portion of the house farthest away from her. The disappearance and reappearance of small objects, often in the presence of the investigators, became this poltergeist's trademark. The poltergeist also viciously attacked the Nevens' infant son. When Dr. Morris arrived to investigate, the Nevens were being driven to a frenzy by spontaneous fires, which often ignited in their baby's crib. The poltergeist ignited one crib several times and incinerated a new crib the same day it was installed in the nursery quarters. Dr. Morris herself observed one of these attacks on the baby, which she described in her report as the "most shocking event I witnessed." The incident occurred one night as Dr. Morris was holding vigil with the family. Dr. Morris writes:

I had been carrying the baby around the house for about 20 minutes, when suddenly he began to cry so loud that I returned him to Brian. He and Jan took the baby into the bedroom to change his diaper. Almost as soon as they entered the bedroom Jan screamed and we all rushed after them. Jan said the baby had started to shake and his eyes had rolled back into his head. When I touched him he was damp and cold but his eyes were focused and he was quiet. Jan went ahead with changing his diaper and when she took it off we all saw twined around his genitals a necklace with a cross which had disappeared from Jan's neck two hours earlier. The young mother fainted and the baby began to cry again.

Sometimes the events transpired so rapidly that it was difficult to keep track of them. For example, on July 21, a few days after Dr. Morris had witnessed the necklace incident, the baby's crib began burning at 9:20 P.M. Only five minutes earlier a collector's coin mysteriously appeared on the floor of the room in which they were all sitting, and more were found later. Moments after that a necklace suddenly appeared by infant Stephen's leg. This PK episode came to a halt soon after when a Bible went up in flames.

At about this time the poltergeist began a new offensive. Now, for the first time, people, including the baby, were actually hit by flying objects. Eggs were especially favored as projectiles and Stephen was hit so hard by one that it resulted in a reddish bruise. These assaults turned into near murderous attacks. Once, upon checking the baby, Brian found his bedcovers wrapped too tightly about his face. An hour later a pillow was suddenly pushed by a mysterious force against Jan's face, nearly smothering her in the process. She couldn't push it away and only Brian's intervention saved her from being asphyxiated.

From that time on, the poltergeist was no longer interested in anything but physically attacking the Nevens. They were hit by innumerable objects, and the blows often caused pain and injury. Finally it ceased employing objects and began hitting the family with physical, though invisible, blows. These blows were so forceful that on one occasion Jan was knocked unconscious. Various members of the family were choked or slapped as well.

Unable to maintain a normal life because of the poltergeist, the Nevens moved to a motel in August, but even there they weren't safe. The poltergeist followed with increasingly frightening attacks until finally it tried to communicate with them.

Dr. Morris writes:

I asked Ben, Brian's father, what had frightened him most throughout the experience. He said that one evening when he and Ebon (Brian's brother) were visiting Brian and Jan they decided to try to communicate with "the spirit." They put pencil and paper on the kitchen table and went to sit in the living room. Returning to check every few minutes they found the following words on various pieces of paper: *he, child, die, baby, back, baby, stay.* Eventually, all except one of the pieces of paper were destroyed by spontaneous fires. Ben added that he thought it had been a mistake to try to communicate since it seemed to make matters worse.

By this time the Nevens realized that they needed more concrete help. Several priests had visited the family previously and had seen the poltergeistery, but they did little to help them. Mediums, mystics, and exorcists all tried their hand at expelling the evil force. Some told the family that the source was their own unconscious conflicts. Mediums saw vicious spirits of the dead attacking the house. The Nevens eventually came to believe that the devil was responsible for the plague so they contacted several church groups that conducted prayer meetings, in order to expel the "demon" through prayer. The poltergeist did subside after the Nevens attended several such meetings, but ultimately made a slow return over the next year. Unable to endure any more, they finally called on Father Karl Pazelt, a Greek Orthodox Catholic priest, who conducted fourteeen exorcism services in the house, which eventually ended the horror.

When news of Father Pazelt's exorcisms was released in the press (this was during the rage over the movie *The Exorcist*), the priest became the center of public controversy. Many fellow priests blatantly denied that there were any such things as poltergeists or "infestations" and harshly criticized Pazelt for his "irresponsible behavior." Another cleric, Richard Byfield, who was obviously familiar with the psychological nature of PK disturbances, accused him of overreacting to a typical poltergeist.

But, one may ask, were the Daly City disturbances those of a "typical" poltergeist?

To be sure, one *can* find a typical poltergeist explanation for this case. Brian was Jewish, his wife was Catholic, and Brian converted to Catholicism during the period of poltergeistery. This indicates that the Nevens were experiencing an intense religious crisis in their personal lives at the time. When I first read of the case I remembered something I had learned while taking a course in marriage counseling. I had been instructed that the time of greatest potential family strife in Jewish-Catholic marriages, especially when the wife is Catholic, is the birth of a baby. Although mutually respecting each other's beliefs, couples often encounter severe emotional problems at this time, since each may consciously or unconsciously desire that the baby be brought up in his or her own religion. This occurs even if neither of them is particularly devout and can cause irreparable damage to some marriages. During the Daly City poltergeist, the baby was the focus of the assaults. Could the poltergeist have been an outlet for hidden conflicts over the child? Could assaults on it have represented a means by which the Nevens "punished" the baby for being the root of the conflict?

No matter what caused the Daly City poltergeist, there is little doubt in my mind that Father Pazelt's actions were, considering his religious training, responsible and compassionate. I feel he bore the brunt of much unfair criticism by clerics and commentators alike, who had no right to talk on a subject (i.e., the poltergeist) about which they had no knowledge. Father Pazelt held up admirably well, however. His reply to his critics was blunt and to the point. No other priest had helped the family, he said. Nor, he flatly stated on a radio program, was he interested in armchair debates over whether such things existed. As he concluded later: "This was a case of possession in which the devil was attacking the family from without. He was working around them, beating and choking them, but he wasn't in their bodies.... They had been looking for help to free them from these evil spirits since 1972, but none of their friends in the clergy could offer a solution."

I am sure the Nevens are thankful that Father Pazelt decided to help.

6

Demonic Poltergeists

Was there really a devil in Daly City? While most experts on psychic phenomena, who generally believe that the poltergeist is merely a vehicle for psychological expression, would eschew the idea, I am far from sure that they are entirely correct. The fact that so many poltergeists show intelligence, carry out complicated and motivated acts, and can even speak or otherwise communicate, leads me to believe that at least a few of them represent some intelligence either independent of the poltergeist victim or perhaps only tenuously connected to the victim.

The Amherst poltergeist of 1878 is one case which suggests that some intelligence lies behind some poltergeist attacks. Never in the recorded history of the paranormal has any other case compared in horror and violence (not even the Bell Witch) to the nightmare which plagued a small two-story cottage in Amherst, Nova Scotia. The victims were Daniel Tweed, a shoe-factory foreman, his wife Olive, two very young sons, George and Willie, and two unmarried sisters-in-law, Jennie and Esther Cox, ages twenty-two and nineteen respectively.

As with so many poltergeists, the Amherst disturbances began unmelodramatically one night in September when Esther leaped out of bed screaming that she felt a mouse stirring under her bedcovers. Both Esther and Jennie searched for the mouse but could not find it. The next night they were awakened again when they heard a rustling noise emanating from a box under the bed. Presuming that a mouse had been caught in it, they dragged the box out; but no sooner had they placed it before them than it began leaping into the air by itself. Their screams brought Tweed to the room, but he only grumbled at the girls' story about the jumping box and went back to sleep.

The next day all was quiet, the incidents of the previous night perhaps even half-forgotten. The family hardly mentioned them to Esther, but the girl, no doubt unnerved by the preceding night's adventures, began to feel ill and had to go off to bed.

At 10 o'clock that night, Esther nudged Jennie (who shared the bed) and in an instant jumped from the bed.

"My God, what is the matter with me? I'm dying," she screamed.

Jennie was no less horrified by the sight. There stood Esther, her hair almost standing on end, her face blood red, her eyes bulging. The rest of the family came in answer to her screams and looked on in horror as Esther's body began to swell. They could do nothing but stand there gawking in disbelief, but were brought back to reality by Esther's incessant screams of pain. At the height of the attack a thundering blow resounded throughout the house, which was so loud that Mrs. Tweed's first thought was that a thunderbolt had struck the house. A quick search revealed that nothing in the house was broken or disturbed. Finally Esther returned to normal and slept peacefully for the rest of the night.

It wasn't until four days later that the next attack began. Esther and her sister had just gone to bed when their bedclothes were torn away from them and sailed through the air before finally falling to the floor. By the time their screams summoned the rest of the family, Esther's body was bloating again. Then the PK began in earnest. As soon as Tweed placed the bedcovers back on the bed, they were ripped off once more. Moments later a pillow was similarly thrown, and as Esther's body swelled, more tremendous raps emanated from the bed.

It was now obvious to Tweed that he needed help badly, so he called in the town physician, Dr. Carritte, hoping that he could diagnose Esther's strange malady. While interested in the medical aspects of the case, the doctor only laughed at Tweed's ghostly story, even though he could see that Esther was in a state of shock. However, Carritte was about to make further medical evaluations when the girl's pillow slid out from under her head, then shifted back again, and continued to move even though Tweed tried to hold it still. At the same time, loud knocking sounds were heard from under the bed, but these soon gave way to scratching noises. Suddenly the family, to their horror, realized that these scratchings represented an attempt to communicate with them and, as they watched, words were slowly etched on the bedroom wall. "Esther Cox, You are Mine to Kill," they warned. No sooner were these ominous words inscribed than the raps commenced again with such fury that a piece of plaster fell from the wall. The commotion lasted for two hours and Dr. Carritte, stunned by what he had seen, promised to return the next day for further investigation.

The Amherst case was certainly a dramatic one. Yet the authenticity of the facts in the case, despite the reserve in which many poltergeist experts hold them, rests on inordinately good evidence. Walter Hubbell, a popular writer of the time, witnessed the poltergeist and collected additional testimony for his book *The Great Amherst Mystery*. Hubbell saw the actual warning words on the wall, which the family had never scraped away. They looked to him like etchings made by a dull metal instrument. We know, then, that the existence of these dreadful words, no matter what their origin, was certainly no myth. Years later the veteran psychic investigator Hereward Carrington made an attempt to track down and interview eyewitnesses to the Amherst poltergeist, and even traveled to Canada to determine if new light could be shed on this most unusual case. Although several decades had passed, Carrington was able to locate several people who vividly recollected their paranormal experiences at the Tweed home. From their testimony Carrington tried to reconstruct the case and came to the conclusion that Hubbell's book, while stressing sensationalism and sometimes exaggerating the facts, was fairly accurate. He ended his Canadian trip certain in his own mind that the Amherst poltergeist was not only genuine, but just as horrendous as its reputation had made it out to be. But let's return to the case itself.

When Dr. Carritte returned the next day, so did the poltergeist. Esther had gone to the cellar shortly after his arrival and immediately complained that a piece of wood had struck her from behind as she was doing her chores. The doctor accompanied her on a return trip to the cellar where a number of potatoes were hurled directly at their heads. Carritte was too shaken to remain in the house any longer, but as he left he heard what he could only describe as sledgehammer-like blows throughout the house.

These poundings soon became a local attraction after news of the disturbances leaked out. (Crowds would collect outside the house in the morning and continue all day.) Eventually the police had to be called in to control the crowds, which were getting out of hand. Tweed was at his wits' end. By this time he began to realize that the PK somehow focused on Esther. Luckily for everyone—except Esther—the girl contracted diphtheria after two months of the horror and was confined to bed for two weeks during which no disturbances were reported. She visited a sister in New Brunswick during her convalescence and quiet returned to the Tweed house.

However, the return of Esther, refreshed and renewed, coincided with the reappearance of the poltergeist, which now exhibited new phenomena. The new attack began when Esther heard a voice claiming to be a spirit calling to her and threatening to set fire to the house. When Tweed was informed of the communication, he only laughed. Perhaps the four weeks of peace had strengthened his incredulousness, but even as Esther told her story a lighted match fell mysteriously from the ceiling directly onto a nearby bed and Tweed's attitude must have changed as he rushed to put out the flame. More lighted matches fell in the room for a full ten minutes, but they were all extinguished before they could do any harm. As if in protest, the poundings began anew, shaking the house with their vigor.

It was at this time that a flustered Jennie Cox again assumed a significant role in the story. Weeks earlier she had tried to communicate with the poltergeist and found that it could respond to simple questions by rapping. Now Jennie began seriously to communicate with the poltergeist. That evening the family listened as it acknowledged, through raps, that it intended to burn down the house. Fires did break out inexplicably for the next three days.

With no other solution in sight, Tweed asked Esther to leave the house.

Esther was immediately taken in by a local Amherst resident named John White, who gave her a job in his restaurant. He soon regretted his offer, though, when the poltergeist started overturning furniture in his restaurant. Once more Esther was dismissed, but was then taken in again, this time by a local man named Captain James Beck, who had been following the case and who was intrigued with the possibility of scientifically studying the phenomena. To his great disappointment, however, little PK occurred in his home.

Since the PK abated while Esther lived at the Beck home, it appeared that the poltergeist was gone, and the Tweeds welcomed Esther back. The poltergeist, however, returned with her and it was at this key point in the case that Walter Hubbell appeared on the scene.

Hubbell was an opportunist from the outset. A sometime magician and actor, he saw great commercial potential in Esther and her "powers," and offered to pay the Tweeds rent money if they would allow him to stay in their home to observe the phenomena. He was richly rewarded, since over the next weeks a knife, several pieces of furniture, and a glass paperweight were all thrown directly at him. During this melee he convinced Tweed to put Esther on the stage. Hopefully the poltergeist would manifest for all to see, he counseled his landlord, and they could both share in the profits. As unbelievable as it seems, Tweed agreed to the idea and made arrangements for Esther to sit on stage and employ her "power" to move props about and otherwise demonstrate her ability for any thrill-seeker willing to pay money for the performance. The plan was a complete fiasco. There sat poor Esther on the stage but, of course, absolutely nothing happened. The crowd demanded the return of its money, and Tweed expelled both Esther and Hubbell from his home in disgust.

The last we know of Esther is from Hubbell, who discovered years later that she had been convicted of burning down an employer's barn and was serving a jail term. Upon her release Esther gradually faded from sight. She was now completely bitter, her life ruined by the poltergeist.

I have recapped the Amherst case at some length to illustrate once again that there is nothing particularly playful about the poltergeist. It is not the harmless ghost as is so often portrayed. Can one believe that Esther, through her own PK, brought such ruin upon herself? Did she destroy her own life in order to vent pent-up hostilities on others? Cases such as the Amherst mystery indicate that, whatever the true nature of the poltergeist may be, the force in some cases is to some degree independent of anyone in the disturbed family. In other words, *in rare instances* the poltergeist may be a true psychic invasion.

One cannot help comparing Esther's seizures to the gyrations of a person allegedly possessed by a demon. According to Roman Catholic tradition, demonic entities can become manifest and plague the living in two ways: by infestation or by possession. Infestation is a blanket term for what we might call hauntings and poltergeist phenomena, i.e., the supernatural invasion of a home by inexplicable sounds, odors, noises, and movement of objects. Possession is, of course, the physical takeover of a victim by an invading entity. Usually this entity will throw its victim's body into convulsions, make the victim scream obscenities, and perpetrate other offensive acts. These two syndromes are not distinct, but often overlap and merge.

The belief that a demon (or god) can take possession of the mind and/or body of a human being is almost universal. Even in widely different cultures the symptoms of the syndrome are remarkably similar. The Reverend John J. Nicola, a Catholic theologian and expert on possession, in his book *Diabolical Possession and Exorcism* (1974), describes several examples of the syndrome from the United States and China. The "ailment" seems identical in both cultures: the victim is taken over by an outside force, screams profanities, and exhibits supernormal powers. Even the rites of exorcism employed by the Catholic Church and in Taoist practices are remarkably similar.

Why should poltergeist experts be interested in a phenomenon that may seem to be only a relic of superstition, culturally evinced belief systems, and religious dogma? There is a simple answer to this question. In cases of demonic possession the victim presumably exhibits supernormal abilities—such as using ESP to pry into the minds of onlookers and using PK to hurl objects about—much the same as the conventional poltergeist does. In fact poltergeist-type phenomena are characteristic of the demonic-possession syndrome. Furthermore it is not rare for a poltergeist victim to believe eventually that he or she is being possessed. In fact William Blatty's *The Exorcist* was based on a genuine 1949 poltergeist case in Georgetown which, long before he popularized it in his book, had been reported in the *Parapsychological Bulletin* (published by the Duke Parapsychology Laboratory) for that year. So, one might ask, do cases of demonic possession represent a genuine psychic syndrome that sheds new light on the poltergeist? If so, what types of explanations can we offer to account for these cases?

The answer to the first question is definitely yes. In fact, demonic possession can only be properly diagnosed by investigators when the victim exhibits types of powers studied in conventional parapsychology. As the syndrome begins, the victim is physically taken over by a new personality, which usually claims to be a demon or a legion of demons. Just because a person makes this claim does not mean that he is genuinely possessed, since people suffering from certain mental disorders often make similar assertions. (For example, in one form of hysteria, the victim may handle deep-seated guilt by punishing himself with delusions that he is becoming possessed.) However, the Roman Catholic doctrines on possession teach that the victim of true demonic possession will perform preternatural phenomena. According to the *Rituale Romanum*, a manual on possession and exorcism, the following symptoms are characteristic of genuine possession: possessed persons speak or understand languages they have never studied; they can foretell future events or exhibit telepathic or clairvoyant abilities; they may display superhuman strength or manifestations beyond their natural age or ability; or they might exhibit any phenomena of a particularly vicious nature which suggest a demonic agency. Perhaps we can include poltergeist phenomena under this last heading.

Some fascinating views on the relationship of parapsychology to the study of possession have been expressed by Corrado Balducci, one-time auditor of the Apostolic Delegation of Jerusalem, Palestine, and Cyprus. In a presentation given before the 1965 International Conference of the Parapsychology Foundation in Le Piol, France, he argued that the possession syndrome is typified by two categories of symptoms. The first, he suggested, are psychogenic in nature: the victim's violent and obscene behavior, the contortions of his body, and the emergence of a foreign personality that competes with his own. In the second category are the psychic effects similar to the ones outlined above. "In fact some of the manifestations common to the demoniac—doubtless the most important—bear a resemblance to the phenomena proper to parapsychology," reported Balducci. "Moreover, the presence of the phenomenology of a parapsychological order, added to that of a psychic (psychological) order, represent, as we have seen, a strong indication in favor of diabolic possession."

With these considerations in mind, one might ask: what evidence actually exists in our enlightened times that demonic possession is not merely a relic of superstitious beliefs? Let us examine two modern cases in which poltergeist-like phenomena were reported as well.

The Earling, Iowa, case (1928) is perhaps the most well-documented account of this rare and bizarre phenomenon ever recorded. The events in this strange case were not publicized at the time, but were recorded in privately printed and circulated pamphlets. The pertinent facts of the case were, however, well observed by several witnesses who placed their testimonies on record, and Father Carl Vogt used them as the basis for his short pamphlet *Begone Satan!* Little was known about the case and copies of the pamphlet were extremely rare when it came to my attention in 1966. But owing to the recent interest in possession and exorcism as a result of Blatty's novel and subsequent motion picture adaptation, the case has now become better known. The chief witnesses were Theophilus Riesinger, a highly regarded priest and exorcist, and Father Steiger, in whose church the rites were performed. (Father Riesinger died in 1941. I have been unable to ascertain the fate of Father Steiger.)

The victim was a forty-year-old woman who was taken from her home and brought to Earling especially for the exorcism. She had suffered from symptoms of demonic possession since the age of fourteen when she began to show a total abhorrence of religious objects. (This is typical of the poltergeist as well, as I stated earlier. Poltergeists will very often focus their destructive energies on religious objects and will sometimes even intensify their fury if a priest attempts to perform religious rites in the house.) Soon after, the woman developed a complete aversion to blessed objects, and began to hear mocking voices taunting her. *Psychiatric examinations showed her to be psychologically normal during the periods between the attacks.* Eventually the victim's psychological symptoms merged into those of a parapsychological order. She proved to several startled onlookers that she could understand foreign languages, could use ESP to discriminate between blessed and unblessed food, and finally took on the personality of a demon that spoke through her. It was then that church officials sanctioned traditional exorcism. At first the rites were held secretly and were witnessed only by Father Riesinger, Father Steiger, who occupied the church and rectory at Earling, his sister, and several nuns. However, the behavior of the possessed woman, and the shouts and screams of the "demons" which emanated daily from the rectory as the exorcisms were performed, alerted the townsfolk to the odd events transpiring in their small town. The collected testimony on the Earling case, therefore, is comprised of the accounts of an impressively large number of witnesses, a few of whom were able to watch the exorcisms in progress. As one of them reported:

Father Theophilus had hardly begun the formula of exorcism in the name of the Blessed Trinity, in the name of the Father, the Son, and the Holy Ghost, in the name of the Crucified Savior, when a hair-raising scene occurred. With lightning speed the possessed dislodged herself from the bed and from the hands of her guards; and her body, carried through the air, landed high above the door of the room and clung to the wall with a tenacious grip. All present were struck with a trembling fear. Father Theophilus alone kept his peace.

"Pull her down. She must be brought back to her place upon the bed."

Real force had to be applied to her feet to bring her down from her high position on the wall. The mystery was that she could cling to the wall at all.

Fearsome noises, howlings, and voices broke out in the rectory when the exorcism was resumed. The sounds did not seem to come from the possessed woman's mouth; instead they broke out in and echoed through the halls, terrifying the nuns. Just as with Esther Cox, the victim's body swelled and bloated, and the woman also showed remarkable ESP ability. But that was only the beginning of the demoniac's power, which later followed Steiger to his own home.

In my discussion on the Minnesota case (see p. 187), I cited strong evidence that people who have an association with a poltergeist often find that it will follow them back to their own homes. I doubt whether the simple "victim-projects-PK" explanation of the poltergeist can account for this phenomenon. If you will recall, two people who tried to help the Minnesota family subsequently went through the ordeal of fighting the poltergeist in their own homes. In the Earling possession case the same thing happened, this time in the homes of Father Steiger and others.

The disturbances at Father Steiger's home began one night when he was awakened by gnawing sounds which seemed to emanate from the walls of his chamber. His first thought was that rats were loose. Yet, he thought to himself, in fourteen years of occupancy he had never heard the likes of these sounds before. When Steiger himself pounded on the walls, eerie noises increased and continued all night, gradually escalating into raps and poundings. Finally Steiger realized that the sounds were being caused by some supernatural force and suspected that they were allied to the exorcism going on in his church. He arose and banished the force by reading religious rites, but the sounds resumed several nights later, this time shaking the room. Father Vogt's booklet goes on to report:

It was learned later that other priests, who had attended the process of expelling the devil, experienced similar inconveniences and annoyances. Even worse things had happened to them. They would not retire after that without having holy water and the stole with them. The noises were often so persistent that one or the other of the priests was obligated to get up at night and seek the place and cause of the disturbances, and only after praying was he able to find peace again. Night prowlers of this kind have been met with in other cases of exorcism even long after the evil spirits had been driven out of the possessed person.

On one occasion Father Steiger was nearly killed when a psychical attack overtook him in his car and caused him to crash.

Finally, after twenty-three days of rituals, the demons who were possessing the woman were exorcised. Later the possession reasserted itself (though this was not mentioned in the pamphlet) and another exorcism had to be performed in Milwaukee. At present a renewed attempt is being made to track down some of the eyewitnesses to these strange events.

There is much common ground between the Earling case and the conventional poltergeist. The poundings on the walls, noises, and levitations are the types of phenomena we most often associate with the poltergeist. Had not the victim *claimed* to be possessed or been "taken over" by another personality, this case might even be classified as a poltergeist.

A clearer illustration of the relationship which exists between possession and poltergeist can be found in those cases where a conventional poltergeist outbreak gradually leads to the victim's becoming, or at least believing himself to be, possessed. In these cases there is no doubt that a more conventional poltergeist was active long before the probable agent began to exhibit possession symptoms. A typical case of this syndrome afflicted a young boy in 1949 in Georgetown. After William Blatty adapted it as the basis of his *The Exorcist*, this became the most popularized poltergeist-possession case ever to reach the public, albeit twenty-five years after it happened.

Although at first few details about the case were reported in the press, the first popular account was published in *Fate* at approximately this same time. However, this account emphasized the poltergeistic PK the Georgetown family was experiencing and made practically no mention of the fact that the agent, a young boy, was exhibiting all the classic symptoms of demonic possession or was undergoing exorcism. The whole story of the Georgetown events did not reach the public until the release of *The Exorcist*. But many of the true details were camouflaged in this book as well. Additional information about the case eventually appeared in *Newsweek*, in Blatty's subsequent book, *I'll Tell Them I Remember You*, and in the popular press during the wave of interest in demonic possession prompted by the movie. However, none of these sources aptly depicted the incredibly gruesome and vicious nature of what began as a conventional poltergeist. These added details only became known when more complete summaries were published, including the eyewitness testimony of family members, friends, physicians, and the accounts of the attending priests. Some of these details appeared in Nicola's *Diabolical Possession and Exorcism*, and later in the January 1975 issue of *Fate* magazine.

The victim was a thirteen-year-old Lutheran boy whose symptoms began shortly after he had begun playing with a Ouija-board. At the time the boy weighed ninety-five pounds and had not yet reached puberty. The diary of the priests who eventually came to aid the family reported that the first peculiar manifestations noted by the boy's family were scratching and rapping sounds which started each evening and went on through the entire night. A picture of Christ which hung on the wall was also heard to rattle about by itself. After ten days the noises ceased, only to recur three days later in the form of squeaky sounds and footsteps, which were heard in the boy's room. The family thought these occurrences were caused by the spirit of a recently deceased relative.

The poltergeist soon became more active. Clothing disappeared and then reappeared in odd places, a chair in which the boy sat overturned by itself, and objects were levitated and floated about in his presence. The poltergeist also followed him to school, where desks and chairs began sliding across the classroom floor. In fact, the PK caused such a disturbance there that the boy had to be removed from school and provided with a private tutor. Although doctors and psychologists examined him at about this time and found nothing abnormal, the beginnings of the possession syndrome became apparent shortly afterward. The boy was levitated on several occasions as he lay in bed; sometimes both he and his mattress would float into the air. This phenomenon occurred repeatedly and was witnessed by several onlookers. It also happened while he was in a hospital being treated for his "illness."

Hoping for some relief, the troubled family invited clergymen to help diagnose the case, and it was apparently the presence of the ministers that prompted the possession to unfold in full fury. The boy suffered spasms, and bounced up and down on his bed as though controlled by puppet strings. Full levitations were interspersed with these unnatural events. Six weeks after the onset of this horror, the boy's seizures abated, but he still went through periods during which he would be possessed by a new personality, and his immature boyish voice would change into, as one account reads, a "... deep, gravelly, raucous voice, using the most obscene and degrading language." Writing would appear on his stomach along with scratches and welts that caused him excruciating pain. Ministers, upon entering the home, were thrown to the floor by invisible blows.

These new developments led the family to turn from their own ministers and call upon the Catholic Church, and after further consideration by church officials, the boy was moved from Georgetown to St. Louis, Missouri, in order that religious exorcism could be conducted by two priests there. During first rites, the ninety-five-pound boy succeeded in ripping a spring from his bed, broke loose from several attendants, and murderously slashed one of the priest's arms. This was only one of many nearly lethal acts he was able to perform with superhuman strength during the possession. The exorcisms lasted ten weeks, during which an incredible array of poltergeist activity and other abnormal phenomena continually startled the priests and other witnesses. The boy's body bloated horribly; he moved his head in a snake-like fashion, spitting with phenomenal accuracy into the eyes of the priests; and the temperature of the room in which he lay turned to icy coldness. Finally the boy began speaking and understanding Latin, though he had never gained even an elementary command of the language. As one eyewitness to these eerie events recalled:

One night the boy brushed off his handlers and soared

through the air at Father Bowdern [one of the exorcists] standing at some distance from his bed [with] the ritual book in his hands. Presumably Father was about to be attacked but the boy got no further than the book. And when his hands hit it—I saw this with my own eyes—he didn't tear the book, he dissolved it! The book vaporized into confetti and fell in small fine pieces to the floor.

Since these attacks were interrupted by periods of normalcy during which the boy was lucid and seemed unaffected by a demon, the exorcist began instructing the victim in the Catholic faith. He was finally admitted to a local hospital (after being denied admittance by many clinics) and there, while he was experiencing an agonizing spasm, an explosion was heard.* This was the end of the ordeal. The boy was restored to normalcy, but with no memory whatsoever of the possession. He soon converted to Roman Catholicism, and has since led a normal and healthy life.

The Reverend John Nicola was able to review the original documents of the case and found them signed by no less than forty-one witnesses.

Neither the Earling nor the Georgetown cases is unique. In fact, Raymond Bayless has written in his *The Enigma of the Poltergeist* that poltergeist-possession may be a distinct syndrome in its own right or may represent a specific *type* of poltergeist. Indeed there are several cases on record indicating the existence of a distinct and consistent poltergeist-possession syndrome. A sampling of them follows.

In Untazell, France, in 1776, several persons went

---

* It is difficult to say with certainty that the explosion coincided exactly with the spasm. It may have occurred shortly after the boy's ordeal.

into convulsions under alleged "demonic control" and their bodies bloated. Independent voices and animal sounds were heard in their presence and furniture was moved telekinetically.

In 1850, again in France, a possession case was reported centering on a victim named Helen Poirier. Her body contorted, she suffered seizures and was pulled along the floor by an invisible force. She also foamed at the mouth and screamed obscenities under the influence of a "demon." Raps were heard, her body levitated, beds shook, and she spoke languages she had never previously studied.

In Illfurth, France, two brothers (aged seven and nine) were possessed from 1864 to 1869. They suffered convulsions, whirled about at fantastic speeds, shouted obscenities, and exhibited a hatred of all religious objects. They also were suddenly able to speak foreign languages, they predicted future events, and objects levitated in their presence.

A young girl was the victim of a poltergeist-possession case reported in 1906–1907 from Natal, South Africa. She suffered convulsions, her body swelled and elongated, odd lumps formed under her skin, and she exhibited a total aversion to religious objects. The girl's levitations were witnessed by a bishop.

An account from France in 1924 reported about a young boy who went into convulsions and reacted violently to anything religious placed near him. Telekinesis was often witnessed by those in his presence.

In 1924-1925 a young novice in Phat-Diem, Vietnam, exhibited classic symptoms of hysteria as raps resounded and apported objects showered about her. Demonic possession was suspected.

It is difficult to tell in these cases whether the poltergeist outbreaks *preceded* the onset of the possession symptoms, or if they occurred only *after* the possession had taken effect. But whatever the case may be, just how can we explain them? Are they merely some bizarre form of poltergeist attack, or do they constitute something strangely different? There are three possible explanations that might account for the poltergeist-possession syndrome.

First, we could argue that the possession symptoms are merely delusions brought on by mental illness, but that the victim uses PK and ESP to reinforce them. People suffering from paranoia, from paranoid-schizophrenia, and from some forms of hysteria often complain that their minds are being invaded by outside entities. It is possible that a few of these unfortunate persons might be gifted with ESP and PK ability and could use it to reinforce their deluded thinking.

Second, we might argue that these cases are really conventional poltergeist outbreaks during which the victim, due to his own religious beliefs or those of persons trying to help, deludes himself into thinking that he or she is possessed and eventually develops symptoms of the syndrome. According to this theory, the possession is really a delusion accompanying the onset of the conventional poltergeist outbreak.*

Last, there remains the demonic theory. That is, poltergeist-possession is a distinct phenomenon in its own right and only superficially resembles the conventional poltergeist. According to this view, the victim is

---

* By the conventional poltergeist I refer to the type that appears to be projected by the PK ability of the agent himself, such as the Miami-Rosenheim cases.

not using his or her own PK to cause the disturbances but, in fact, an outside entity (or demon) is the perpetrator of the PK. This is, of course, the traditional Roman Catholic viewpoint.

Let us take a look at each of these theories and see how well they cover the facts.

At the end of the nineteenth century it was already known that hysterics sometimes believed themselves to be possessed. So common was hysteria in Victorian times that it occupied a great deal of Freud's attention; in fact, his eventual understanding of the nature of the subconscious was largely due to his researches into this disorder. During hysterical attacks, the subject often undergoes marked physical and/or psychological dysfunctions, although there are no organic reasons for them. The victim may suffer aches and pains, paralysis, loss of feeling, dizziness, and blindness. Amnesia, somnambulism, and other memory disturbances are also complications of the ailment. All these symptoms are purely psychosomatic in nature. Hysteria is a complex disorder but, simply stated, one cause of hysteria is unconscious guilt or conflict. In some cases the victim knows or deludes himself into believing that he is gravely guilty of some moral transgression and proceeds to institute a form of self-punishment. For example, a woman of strong religious background might have been told during childhood that dancing is sinful. Yet one day, years later, she goes to a dance and the next morning finds her legs paralyzed. Her paralysis is actually only psychosomatic, and her symptom is called a "hysterical reaction" or a "conversion reaction."

Years ago it was not uncommon for these attacks of guilt to be manifested in the form of pseudo-possession.

In his *L'Automatisme Psychologique* (1888) the pioneer French psychiatrist Pierre Janet described many cases of pseudo-possession that he had clinically observed. His most famous case was that of Achilles, a country peasant who showed all the classical physical symptoms of possession when he consulted Janet: He was suffering convulsions and contortions of the body; a "demon entity" took over his voice and cursed him; and so on. At face value these symptoms were identical to those of classical possession with one notable exception—the victim exhibited no supernormal powers. Janet soon discovered that Achilles had developed his malady after cheating on his wife. When the peasant was assured of divine forgiveness for his guilt-inflicting deed, the "possessing entity" departed. It was his own guilt, of course, that caused Achilles to punish himself. Since Achilles was a religious man, what better way to scourge himself than by deluding himself into believing he was the victim of a demonic attack?

In many of the poltergeist cases I have described in this book, it appears as though the victims may have been hysterical. For instance, Esther Cox's bloated body and Karin's nervousness are symptomatic of hysteria. Could it be, then, that the poltergeist-possession victims are really just hysterics who are able to use ESP and PK to reinforce their delusions?

There is some evidence which supports this theory. The physical symptoms suffered by the victims of hysteria, the poltergeist, and possession are all very similar. There is also a striking sex bias in all three categories. In both poltergeist and possession cases, female victims far outnumber males. Coincidentally, hysteria is also experienced more often by women. We know, too, that hysterical attacks are much more common in adolescents and young adults than in mature individuals. This is also true of poltergeist and possession victims. Finally, there are fewer possession cases being reported today than in earlier times. But this could be due to the fact that religious authorities prefer to keep these cases out of public knowledge, so an accurate count is hard to make. Nonetheless, some theologians, such as the Reverend Mr. Nicola, have pointed out that possession cases are increasingly rare in contemporary Western culture. Hysteria, too, has been called the "illness of the uninformed" and is progressively becoming less frequent in our society as the educational level of the general public rises.

However, I am not of the opinion that the hysteria-PK/ESP hypothesis can account for all demonic poltergeist-possession cases. Any person so unstable as ultimately to develop hysterical traits would reveal this instability during psychological testing or while undergoing psychiatric observation. Psychiatric evaluations were made of the victims in both the Earling and Georgetown cases, and they were found to be essentially normal. Any mental dysfunction so great as to cause the total personality disintegration associated with possession, or prompt the hostilities and aggression needed to unleash the poltergeist, would certainly be revealed during psychiatric evaluations. No such abnormalities were apparent in the Georgetown case, so this case was more than a mere poltergeist.

The symptoms of hysteria and true possession *are* sometimes dissimilar as well. The demoniac is horrified as he begins to realize what is happening to him, while the hysteric is curiously indifferent, passive, and unconcerned about his malady. This puzzling attitude that hysterics often develop toward themselves was given the label *la belle indifference* by French doctors, because it was so common. Second, hysteria is projected inwardly. The victim wishes to punish himself and no one else. Yet victims of diabolical possession are vicious and even murderous. In the Earling case the demoniac almost succeeded in killing Father Steiger while he was driving in his car, and the Georgetown boy slashed one arm, broke the bones of two attendants, and almost killed his mother. This behavior is notably different from the neurotic self-afflicting plight of the hysteric.

Finally, there is no evidence that hysterics are prone to having psychic abilities. Although the early parapsychologists thought a relationship might exist, contemporary evaluations have shown that persons with neurotic tendencies invariably do poorly on ESP tests. How, then, can we propose the theory that demonic possession is really a rare form of hysteria? To my mind, while this explanation is theoretically possible, the hysteria-ESP/PK explanation simply cannot account for the poltergeist-possession syndrome.

As mentioned above, another theory which might account for the poltergeist-possession syndrome is that the possession aspect arises only after the poltergeist has begun its siege. In other words, the subject only deludes himself into believing that he is possessed by outside entities, most commonly as a result of his own religious beliefs. Some cases can be easily explained this way. The Georgetown victim showed no signs of possession until *after* ministers had been asked to aid in the case. It is also likely that in some cases the poltergeist victims were thrown into hysteria *by* the poltergeist. These attacks might have too frequently been diagnosed as demonic possession by onlookers who then convinced the victims to accept the same interpretation.

This may have happened in the 1924 Phat-Diem case cited above. In this case PK phenomena broke out in a convent where one of the novices was continually pelted by sticks and stones. Soon other missiles were thrown, bottles were smashed, and laughter and other bizarre noises were heard constantly. The young girl on whom the poltergeist focused soon became hysterical because of the strange events. Other novices were convinced that they were being attacked by the devil, and soon there was a contagion of hysterical possession. Religious exorcism eventually brought order back to the convent. It is more than likely that the presence of a conventional—and otherwise undiabolical—poltergeist ignited these exaggerated emotional reactions.

In the Georgetown case, too, it was only after the family considered the possibility of possession that their son began to display all the classical symptoms. He may have only been responding to his parents' beliefs or suggestions.

However, when we start comparing the types of PK effects utilized by the conventional poltergeist to those employed by the poltergeist-possession we begin to see a real difference in the syndromes. Admittedly, many symptoms of poltergeist-possession *are* identical to those noted during conventional poltergeist attacks. These PK effects include the telekinetic movement of objects, odd noises, and raps. Yet poltergeist-possession cases are also characterized by several types of phenomena that are very rare and atypical of the classical poltergeist. For example, a victim of demonic possession often exhibits two extremely curious phenomena: (1) the ability to speak or understand languages never previously studied and (2) frequent levitation.

To my knowledge there has never been a conventional poltergeist case recorded in which the agent suddenly developed the facility to speak or understand a foreign language. This suggests that the poltergeist-possession is a distinct phenomenon in its own right. Its common resemblances to the classical poltergeist might be more superficial than real. Similarly the levitation of the human body is only infrequently noted in classical poltergeist cases. In his encyclopedic *Can We Explain the Poltergeist?* A. R. G. Owen does cite several such cases, but he found that the vast majority of them were recorded in cases in which witchcraft or possession was suspected. There were a few levitations reported in more conventional cases, but the only modern report with which I am familiar is the 1934 Poona poltergeist. This case, reported from Poona, India, was included in Father Herbert Thurston's *Ghosts and Poltergeists*. This poltergeist, which focused on an eight-year-old boy, was particularly fierce and assaulted the child with rocks as well as other objects. On at least one occasion the boy was totally levitated. The following is an eyewitness account of the incident:

I carefully investigated a remarkable case here in Poona a few years ago.... Briefly I may say that when I first visited the house ... the testimony of various witnesses convinced me that it was impossible to attribute all the amazing disturbances to their son, a lad of eight, around whom these activities seemed to gather. I placed the lad (stark naked) on a small bed, felt his pulse, and told him to "lie down quietly." I then closed the door and windows and sat down on a chair in a corner of the room. I looked at my watch; it was exactly 1:30 P.M. I put a sheet over him. In about fifteen minutes I saw the bedclothes pulled off the bed on which the lad was lying, the bed was pulled into the middle of the room, and the lad actually lifted off the bed and deposed gently on the floor. The lad could feel the arm of an unseen person at work. A bottle of ink that was on the table by the window was flung towards me, and so was a glass paper-weight, narrowly missing my head....

While this account may test our credibility today, *the levitation of the human body is one of the most prevalent PK effects recorded during possession cases.* It was not only witnessed at Earling, but also at Georgetown in 1949. Father Nicola, in his *Diabolical Possession and Exorcism*, discusses two other modern eyewitness accounts of levitation. How do skeptics explain these incidents? They usually compare the levitation of the demoniac to the body-arching spasms that have been observed in patients suffering hysterical or epileptiform seizures. During these seizures the body may arch almost into a complete semicircle, with only the victim's toes and top of the head touching the ground. It has been quite seriously proposed that this body-arching is malobserved during alleged possession cases as full levitation by credulous witnesses overwrought by their beliefs and by what they are seeing. I don't think any comment need be made on how inadequate this theory is.

There are a few secondary phenomena which frequently occur during poltergeist-possession cases but rarely occur during more conventional outbreaks. The production of independent voices is much more common during possession cases, although this phenomenon has also been reported during some conventional cases.

Possessed victims often exhibit superhuman strength, while poltergeist victims do not. The vomiting of pins and other matter, and the production of PK effects over great distances, are more commonly reported in possession cases than in typical poltergeist reports. Finally, poltergeists are rarely personally harmful, even if they are destructive, and are short-lived. Possession-poltergeists are the exact opposite. They are not only destructive but can be murderous. They may also go on for years. Therefore, while the conventional poltergeist and the possession-poltergeist resemble each other in many ways, there are enough points of difference between them to indicate that they are separate syndromes.

Last, we come to the orthodox Catholic viewpoint, that poltergeist-possession is caused by the physical intervention of demonic agencies into human affairs. Not only is this interpretation maintained by the Catholic Church, but similar views have been noted in many non-Christian societies. The Chinese, for example, hold identical beliefs and are also familiar with the poltergeist-possession syndrome. Laurence G. Thompson, in his *Chinese Religions: An Introduction*, describes an exorcism he saw performed in 1961. The possessed person acted in exactly the same way that possessed victims are described in contemporary American accounts.

The theory that some sort of "outside agency" or demon is behind the poltergeist-possession attack can explain many puzzling aspects of the syndrome. It can, for instance, explain the victim's ability to understand or use foreign languages. (Note that I am not saying *what* this agency is—demon, spirit, or other—only that it is an intelligence or will independent of the victim's mind.) After all, even if we accept that poltergeist agents have remarkable psychic ability, ESP cannot explain the possessed person's ability to speak a language that he has never learned. The "outside-agency" theory can also explain the frequent production of independent voices and PK effects over great distances. And the demon theory can also account for the murderous nature of the poltergeist-possession victim.

Nonetheless, there are several arguments against the demon theory. Although demonic possession is a universal phenomenon, its victims do betray a cultural bias in their speech and actions. For example, if you compare conversations recorded between demons and exorcists in Western cases to those recorded between demons and priests in Oriental cases, you will see that the entities always conform to local customs and beliefs.* This would indicate that possession syndrome is linked to the culture and beliefs of the victims.

It is obvious that in poltergeist-possession cases we are dealing with some entity which produces the poltergeist phenomena, but which is both dependent and independent of the agent's mind. Just what this intelligence might be is a mystery that I will explore in the next chapter.

No discussion of the poltergeist would be complete without some comment on "demonic infestation." Poltergeists especially like to disrupt the lives of the

* Lengthy conversations between demons and exorcists in Western cases are printed in Corrado Balducci, *Gli Indemoniati* and in *Begone Satan!* Conversations recorded during Chinese exorcisms are printed in John Nevius, *Demon Possession and Allied Themes.*

intensely religious. These cases often resemble traditional poltergeist cases, but there are notable differences. First, they usually do not focus on a disturbed adolescent and may continue for years and far longer than the usually short life of the typical poltergeist. Some of them will attack an individual living alone instead of a family. Here are just a few examples.

In 1138 the house of Bishop Hugh of Maris was bombarded by showers of stones. In the 1100s St. Godric's monastery was continually attacked by a poltergeist. Stones barraged it, his box of altar-beads was thrown about, religious objects were constantly defaced, and every nonstationary object in his cell was hurled at him. In 1716 the home of the intensely religious Reverend Samuel Wesley was disturbed, as I have chronicled in Chapter 2. A German clergyman's home was thrown into disorder by a poltergeist for several months in 1718, and in 1753 violent poltergeist-mediated bell-ringings were reported from the Russian Monastery of Tzarekonstantinoff. Spontaneous fires, telekinesis, and mysterious sounds were reported in 1905 from Binbrook Rectory, Lincolnshire, England. A very active poltergeist plaguing the home of a clergyman was reported by Dr. James Hyslop of the American Society for Psychical Research, who witnessed the phenomenon in 1911. *Years* of poltergeist activity began in 1913 at Weston Vicarage in Great Britain. Months of poundings, bell-ringings, and other noises began in 1930 at Watton Vicarage in England, and were witnessed by the church's minister and his family.

Of course, it is hard to judge just how much more often poltergeists occur in religious settings than in private homes. But throughout the history of Western

culture, saints and ascetics have endured the ordeal of
the poltergeist and its infestations. As the examples
above show, poltergeists also exhibit a marked tendency
to single out religious institutions.

A typical example of this type of "personal poltergeist," as I call them, was recorded by John Marie
Vianney, the curé of Ars, who after his death (1859) was
canonized by the Catholic Church. His life was as
remarkable as the poltergeist which tormented him.
Although never a very astute scholar (he barely
commanded Latin), his extraordinary piety soon
endeared him to his parishioners. He lived in poverty,
rarely ate, and often scourged his own body in order to
force his mind away from worldly preoccupations. He
was intensely devoted to spiritual contemplation and,
when not serving his congregation, spent his time in
deepest religious meditation and prayer. Michel de Saint
Pierre, who wrote an excellent biography on Vianney
entitled *The Remarkable Curé of Ars*, also chronicles
several well-documented accounts of the curé's ESP
ability.

It was during the course of the curé's intense religious
life at Ars that the "Grappin" (a nickname he gave the
devil) came to plague him. He was literally assaulted by
the poltergeist for several years. Luckily the curé left an
account of the manifestations, which began with
conventional rapping:

The first time the devil came to torment me was one night
at 9 o'clock, just as I was about to go to bed. Three loud knocks
resounded on my courtyard door, as if someone wanted to break
it in with an enormous sledge-hammer. I immediately opened
my window and asked: *Who is it?* ... But I saw nothing and

went quietly to bed.... I was not yet asleep when three more knocks made me jump. These were more violent than the first, and struck not against the outside door but against the one at the foot of the stairs leading to my room. I got up and cried out a second time: *Who is there?* No one answered.

When the noises began, I imagined it was some thieves who wanted the beautiful ornaments of *Monsieur le Vicomte of Ars,* and I thought it would be wise to take precautions. I asked two courageous men to come and sleep at the rectory, to lend me a strong hand in case of need. They came several nights in a row; they heard the noise but discovered nothing, and were convinced that this uproar had been caused by something other than the malice of men. I soon became certain of it myself, for one winter night when it had snowed hard, there were three heavy knocks in the middle of the night. I jumped hurriedly from my bed, seized a lamp and went down into the courtyard, thinking I would surely find the culprits in flight and intending to call for help. But to my surprise I saw nothing, I heard nothing, and what is more, I found no footprints in the snow....

I then had no further doubt but that it was the devil who wanted to frighten me....

This account proves that the curé was neither a credulous nor a poor observer. He accepted the idea that something supernatural was the cause of the disturbances only after considering several normal possibilities. And his endeavors to catch the "intruders" show that the curé had a keenly rational mind.

The raps heralded more active poltergeistic assaults. The curé's curtains were torn and emitted fearful sounds, which the curé first thought were being caused by rats. Door latches were shaken, thunderous raps shook the entire rectory, independent voices were heard, insulting and threatening him, and his furniture was continually shifted about the room. The curé was not the only witness to the poltergeist, for several of the townsfolk were also able to watch the Grappin's actions.

The curé's poltergeist usually had a purpose when it attacked. Vianney seldom slept, since he preferred to spend as many waking hours as possible in religious service. Like many other ascetics, he avoided engaging in any pleasurable activity that might distract him from God. The poltergeist invariably struck when the curé lay down for a few hours of rest. One of his most devoted admirers, Catherine Lassagne, once noted in her diary that "M. Le Curé has asked us to broaden his straw mat because the devil threw him out of his bed. 'I did not see the Grappin', he added, 'but he grabbed me several times and threw me out of my bed.' "

The curé often told Catherine about the poltergeist's actions, which at times became active in the confessional. And like many other more conventional poltergeists, the curé's Grappin singled out religious items for specific defacement. As Michel de Saint Pierre records in his biography of the curé:

Another of the devil's phantasies—one of the vilest we have ever heard of—led him to profane an image of the Blessed Virgin representing the Annunciation. It was a picture that hung on the wall at the turn of the rectory stairs and Father Vianney was very fond of it. Seeing the particular veneration the good Curé had for this image, the *Grappin* covered it each night with mud and filth. Wash it as he might, the Curé would still find it the next morning "blacker and more contaminated than the day before." Things reached such a point that he decided to have the picture removed. Such a course sorely grieved him, as it symbolized a victory for the unnatural force. The testimony on this story is as indisputable as possible.

Father Renard (the Curé's assistant) declared that he had seen the picture sullied to the point "that the Blessed Virgin's face was no longer recognizable."

By the end of the curé's life, scores of fellow priests, visitors, penitents, and peasants had spent some time in his quarters and could testify firsthand about the poltergeistery. The case of the curé of Ars is typical of the poltergeists that tormented many saints and mystics. St. Martin, St. Teresa of Ávila, St. Benedict, and the mystic Teresa Higginson all reported minor poltergeistic molestations.

7

The Intelligence behind the Poltergeist

Even though we do know a great deal about the poltergeist, its basic nature is still a mystery to us. How is it projected? Where does its energy come from? What intelligence directs it? We have no definite answers to any of these mysteries, and can only conjecture what the solutions might be. Nonetheless there are two myths about the poltergeist that should be properly dismissed. First of all, there is no reason to believe that all poltergeists are the same. There might be various kinds, which we lump together simply because their phenomena appear similar. I think I can make this point a little clearer by using an analogy from medicine. Brain toxins, schizophrenia, vitamin deficiency, and even hypoglycemia can all produce similar symptoms. Yet the causes and nature of these disorders are entirely different. We can probably apply this paradox to the poltergeist. Second, there is no reason to assume that there is but one mechanism responsible for the poltergeist. Various poltergeist cases might be caused by diverse psychic processes. Because in one case an adolescent uses his PK to unleash a poltergeist does not mean that this is necessarily true of all poltergeists.

To my mind there seem to be two basic types of poltergeists. I call the classical "adolescent poltergeist" the *Type I* poltergeist, although this variety can focus on older persons as well. In these cases the PK displays usually involve the movement of objects in the vicinity of the child or disturbed adult, around whom the effects generally center. It will not usually occur unless that person is physically present. Type I poltergeists seem devoid of sophisticated intelligence and their behavior is often rather childish. Type I poltergeists do not carry out any acts which are beyond the physical capabilities of the agent. In contrast, *Type II* poltergeists are more violent and show a definite intelligence. They communicate, attack, and reveal some level of external will. I refer to this type of poltergeists as the "entity-poltergeist," since it appears that some intelligent entity is operative in this case. Such PK displays as teleportation, bodily levitation, the movements of huge objects, personal attacks, and fire-setting are typical Type II phenomena. Type II poltergeists can and do carry out acts seemingly beyond the physical capabilities of the agent.

Not much needs to be said about the intelligence behind the Type I poltergeist. The research of such parapsychologists as W. G. Roll has done much to help us understand these cases. There can be little doubt that during the conventional poltergeist the agent projects PK, or a PK-type field, in order to vent his unconscious hostility. Roll discovered that objects closest to the agent are most likely to be disturbed, that the objects move in a uniform direction, and that as they travel they lose force. All these facts support the PK-projection theory. Roll has postulated two different mechanisms that may account for these PK-projections. These he calls the "psi-field" hypothesis and the "moving-beam" hypothesis. Both theories are similar in nature and simply argue that, during the poltergeist attack, the agent projects PK as a field or beam around him. Any objects coming into contact with the field are likely to be moved.

In fact, Roll is not comfortable with the term "poltergeist," since it implies that some intelligence other than the agent's own is responsible for the disturbance. He has suggested instead that we call these phenomena *RSPK*, which stands for *recurrent spontaneous psychokinesis*. As he writes in his book *The Poltergeist*:

I do not know of any evidence for the existence of the poltergeist as an incorporeal entity other than the disturbances themselves, and these can be explained more simply as PK effects from a flesh and blood entity who is at their center. This is not to say that we should close our minds to the possibility that some cases of RSPK might be due to incorporeal entities. But there is no reason to postulate such an entity when the incidents occur around a living person. It is easier to suppose that the central person is himself the source of the PK energy.

Since parapsychologists usually define psychokinesis as the direct influence of mind over material objects, RSPK is a good term for the Miami and Seaford disturbances. There was no intelligence at work in these cases other than the primitive and consciously repressed urge to destroy that we all harbor in our subconscious minds.

Roll does admit, though, that sometimes objects will move even when the agent is *not* present. To account for these incidents he suggests: "It seemed as if the poltergeist person somehow imbued the objects with a special property or quality which made them sensitive even to the weak kind of PK any of us may be producing."

These comments are all applicable to Type I poltergeists. But what about Type II cases? How do we explain the apportation of objects from distant locations, poltergeistic eruptions in the homes of peripheral witnesses, fire-setting poltergeists, apparitions, and poltergeists which speak or otherwise communicate? How does Roll account for these phenomena? During Type II attacks it appears as though there is an entity, independent of the agent's unconscious mind, at work master-minding the disruptions. It is the nature of this entity that I would now like to explore.

The fact that poltergeist outbreaks usually center on one specific individual does not rule out the possibility that in some cases the PK activity might be directed by an independent agency. One probable case of this type was reported by Hereward Carrington, who was probably the most versatile and experienced psychical investigator in America. Although he was a seasoned investigator, he only confronted the poltergeist once in his career … when he himself was the focus!

The PK began after Ida P., a friend of Carrington's, died. He did not know of her death until one day when he strongly desired to phone her. He had not seen her for a year, and the woman who answered the call told him that Ida had died the day before.

Shortly after making the call, Carrington began to feel a presence in his apartment. It was unmistakable. (I should note here that Carrington had a cold disposition, a phenomenally critical mind, and often exposed fake mediums.) The entity he sensed in his apartment was not ever-present, but manifested itself sporadically, moving from one section in the apartment to another. Neither was he the only one who felt this invisible presence. Carrington writes in his book *The Psychic World* that a neighbor entered the apartment during this time and mentioned that he thought "someone" was standing in a small alcove in the room. This was the same place that Carrington had also felt the presence on several occasions. This odd invasion lasted for three days during which time mild poltergeist phenomena began to occur.

"During those three days," Carrington recorded, "I had 'rappings' at irregular intervals all over the place— on the walls, the floor, and the furniture. These were sometimes quite loud and utterly unlike anything heard before or since."

A note on the piano was struck, after which the rappings and the presence immediately ceased. To Carrington it was as though something was trying to attract his attention and was only quieted after it had succeeded. Carrington concluded, "...I have come no nearer any other solution of the problem since then."

In this case, the poltergeist activity was linked to some uncanny "presence." Carrington did not necessarily feel that the presence was that of his disembodied friend, but the thought—and the coincidence between the outbreak and her death—naturally passed through his mind. Did Carrington project his own PK to cause the raps, or was the PK produced by an outside intelligence? Or was it perhaps a mixture of both? There are many cases like this one on record. I know of a poltergeist that centered on a young woman who, shortly before her wedding, received the news that her fiancé had been killed. Shortly after, a poltergeist broke out in her home, which dissipated only after many months. Was there a link between the poltergeist and the dead man? We shall never know. Another case in which a discarnate entity might have been active was observed by the late Bishop James Pike and is chronicled in his book *The Other Side*.

The poltergeist began only after a family tragedy. There had been considerable discord between Pike and his drug-experimenting son and, in an effort to improve their relationship, Pike had rented an apartment for the two of them in Cambridge, England. Soon after, young Jim killed himself in a New York hotel room during a short trip to the United States. Two weeks later the bereaved bishop returned to his Cambridge apartment, where the poltergeist began its antics. The minister found books, postcards, and safety pins lying about the apartment always opened or placed to form a 140-degree angle. Also set at the same angle was his clock, which had been stopped at 8:19 o'clock—the approximate time when Jim had killed himself. More PK acts followed. Fresh milk quickly soured, crayon marks defaced the walls, objects repositioned themselves, things disappeared and reappeared later, and Pike's assistant's hair was singed while she was in the apartment.

Since Pike was familiar with the science of parapsychology, he sought the aid of Canon John Pearce-Higgins of the Churches' Fellowship for Psychical and Spiritual Studies in Great Britain, who urged him to try to determine if the personality of his son were indeed trying to communicate with him. It was at Pearce-Higgins's suggestion that Pike began to engage in his well-publicized and controversial experiments with such well-known mediums as Ena Twigg, George Daisley, and Arthur Ford, during which time he came to believe that he had in fact communicated with his son. Shortly thereafter Pike himself died from exposure when he became lost in the Israeli desert during a trip to the Holy Land. It is perhaps significant that Pike, whose whole life had been one of religious questioning, should die so soon after having finally received personal evidence of that most sacred of Christian beliefs—personal immortality.

In this case it is hard to dismiss the possibility that an outside intelligence was trying to catch the clergyman's attention. Or could Pike have used his own PK to create the poltergeist? The case could be argued either way. On one hand, the events usually occurred when Pike was out of the apartment, which is atypical of the conventional poltergeist. But it is also true that Pike was laden with guilt over his son's death. This is exactly the sort of disturbed psychological setting that might set off a poltergeist.

So just what type of setting really does unleash the poltergeist? Roll and Bender have concentrated almost solely on the role that denied feelings of hostility play in the etiology of the poltergeist. But other factors come into play as well. As I review the cases reported in this book, it is clear that one of the following three characteristics was usually present and related to the onset of the poltergeist: (1) denial of feelings of frustration and hostility; (2) sexual conflicts and the onset of sexual maturity; (3) intensely religious lifestyles or conflicts.

Now, one might ask, do these three characteristics have anything in common? The answer is yes. It is *guilt*. All three settings are hotbeds of unmanageable guilt. In the Miami and Seaford cases, the repressed hostility and aggression of the adolescent agents resulted in the poltergeist activity. This type of repression does not occur because the children are afraid that they will be punished for any overt act of defiance. These feelings are denied because the agent would react with intense guilt if he acknowledged his true feelings. It is this guilt that is being repressed more than the actual frustration. The onset of sexuality can also be a source of guilt. In the Victorian age sex was seen as dirty. You could not even talk about it. It was considered loathsome. Girls were more often the victims of guilt about their awakening sexual desires than were boys, and this may be why more girls than boys became poltergeist agents in those years. However, in the light of our more enlightened attitudes toward sex and sex education this problem is not as acute as it was in previous years. The fact that just as many boys as girls become poltergeist victims today might also be because of increased sexual equality. Religious convictions and resulting conflicts also can cause intense guilt feelings, especially if the sufferer feels that his human feelings and way of living are inconsistent with the way he thinks he *should* behave. In fact, many psychologists hold that religion is in part a vehicle for the self-enforcement of moral codes through fear and guilt.

Guilt is a much more complicated and forceful influence in our lives than most of us realize. According to Freud, a great deal of our behavior is the result of unconscious guilt. It can even cause the mind to punish itself. For example, in some cases of hysteria the victim will become paralyzed in order to punish himself for some real or imagined moral transgression. (As an example, see the case of Achilles recounted in chapter 6.) So the poltergeist might be an expression of guilt, not hostility. Since in so many cases the PK centers on an agent, Roll believes that this indicates that the person is projecting the poltergeist away from himself. But in the cases of Eleanore Zugun and Esther Cox it most viciously attacked the agents themselves. Could these attacks have been a form of self-punishment? Bishop Pike acknowledged that he was plagued by intense guilt feelings after the death of his son. Could he have unleashed the poltergeist to punish himself? Carrington could also have felt guilty because he had not seen Ida before her death.

Despite all the evidence supporting a completely psychological interpretation of the poltergeist, a few contemporary parapsychologists still argue that some poltergeists might represent a greater enigma. Dr. Ian Stevenson, who heads a division of parapsychology at the University of Virginia Medical School, has been one of the most vocal proponents of this view. In his paper "Are Poltergeists Living or Are They Dead?" which was published in the July 1972 issue of the *Journal of the American Society for Psychical Research*, Stevenson pointed out several cases which he feels cannot be explained by the "projected-repression" theory. One case he cites in his report centered on a boy named Sisir Kamur and his family in West Bengal.

The first indication that a poltergeist was imminent came when Sisir was playing with his friends. Upon hearing something fall in an adjoining room, he went in to discover small objects spilled over the floor. Soon the events became more dramatic, and bottles and other objects were seen thrown about. The police were called in and a team monitored the house, but their presence did nothing to deter the poltergeist.

Apports were frequently reported in the Kamur case. Soon, however, an entity, apparently the boy's deceased father, seemed to be trying to communicate with the family. The presence of the father and other entities became evident in a variety of ways. For example, apparitions were often seen. One witness saw a shadowy female form, which was also seen by Sisir. Another witness saw an apparition picking up bricks. (This was an intriguing observation, since bricks were often thrown during the attack.) After religious rites were conducted in the house the phenomena ceased. Stevenson writes about such cases in his *Journal* article:

Sometimes there occur physical phenomena during poltergeist disturbances which we can only with difficulty ascribe to living human agency, even when equipped with important paranormal powers. I refer to those cases in which an object is observed flying through the air and suddenly changes its speed or trajectory. Sometimes the objects turn at a sharp angle and continue flight in a new direction. On other occasions they are reported to show abrupt variation in speed of flight. They seem to hurtle through the air, then suddenly to float to a gentle rest.... I think such cases suggest some discarnate agency actually carrying the objects transported or somehow otherwise controlling their flight. I have not myself been able to imagine how such effects could be produced solely by the unconscious mind of the living agent.

Actually Stevenson's view is not unequivocal. Since PK can move objects, disrupt equipment, and even levitate furniture, I see no reason why PK from a living person could not control the movement of objects in more bizarre ways. After all, we have no knowledge whatsoever of the potential power or nature of psychokinesis, so we should not limit its powers to what we *think* it can do. But Stevenson has made the important point that in some cases it would seem that an intelligent will masterminds the poltergeist.

In reviewing the poltergeist we are confronted by a number of paradoxes. So, before explaining what I think a poltergeist might be, let me sum up these puzzles:

1. Some poltergeists are obviously produced by an agent, yet others show an external will. While some center on a disturbed adolescent, others do not, even though they display similar types of PK effects.

2. Although in most poltergeist cases the phenomena center on or around a specific individual, at times the poltergeist perpetrates acts which are not easily explained by the theory that this person is projecting his own PK.

3. Although most poltergeists are produced by the living, in some cases apparitions are seen and communications from the dead are received.

Actually, all of these apparent contradictions bring us to one crucial issue. Somehow the poltergeist is simultaneously both dependent and independent of the will and personality of the victim. This leads to my own theory about the poltergeist which, in its simplest form, can be stated this way: It is my belief that the poltergeist is caused and directed by a portion of the agent's mind and will, which can function *independently* of the mind and motivation that gave it birth. In other words, once the poltergeist is unleashed it is no longer dependent on the unconscious, which engendered it. It can take on a consciousness, will, direction, motivation, and intelligence of its own. This is why it may or may not show independent intelligence.

This theory is not entirely novel, and even Nandor Fodor eventually came to accept it as a partial explanation for the poltergeist. For example, in his analysis of the Bell Witch case, which he includes in his book *Haunted People*, he stated:

I began to wonder whether indeed a devastating shock might not produce a kind of psychic lobotomy, tearing loose part of the mental system and leaving it floating free, like a disembodied entity, but still capable of personality development, as any autonomous complex would be, though on a different, apparently fourth-dimensional level (whatever that may mean) plane of activity.

Fodor, who himself borrowed the theory from a suggestion made to him by his friend Dr. Maxwell Telling, also conjectured that this complex might "organize itself into an independent personality." But is there any empirical evidence available in support of this theory? I believe there is.

For years psychical investigators have been aware of a strange phenomenon in which an element of an individual's consciousness appears to detach itself physically from the body and continues to function independently of it for a short time. This phenomenon is called the out-of-the-body experience (OOBE) and occurs when the individual is ill, or falling asleep. It can also be caused by physical shock. Some people even have such experiences purely spontaneously. For example, the following is a typical description of this experience, recounted by a woman who wrote to me years ago:

... in the early hours of the morning I was suddenly wide awake, but to my amazement, I was hovering between the ceiling and the bed. I looked down and saw myself on the bed. I was still attached to it in some queer way. I was swaying first towards the ceiling, then down a little, then gently towards the window. This gentle floating feeling, quite pleasant but bewildering, kept on for some time. Always I felt as if attached to my body somehow. I was a little scared. I kept thinking "Please let me go back"—and suddenly I was! I was never conscious of the journey back, though.

Many people have had this experience, and one English researcher found that over 20 percent of those he questioned claimed to have had at least one OOBE during their lifetime. An American researcher found that 27 percent of his respondents reported that they had had the sensation of being "outside" of their bodies. This experience is more than merely a dream or hallucination, and some people undergoing it have been able to prove the reality of the experience in a variety of ways. For example, the following narrative from Celia Green's *Out-of-the-Body Experiences* cannot be dismissed as being due to a dream or a hallucination:

I was in a hospital having an operation for peritonitis; I developed pneumonia and was very ill. The ward was L shaped; so that anyone in bed at one part of the ward could not see round the corner.

One morning I felt myself floating upwards, and found myself looking down on the rest of the patients. I could see myself, propped up against pillows very white and ill. I saw the sister and nurse rush to my bed with oxygen. Then everything went black. The next I remember was opening my eyes to see the sister bending over me. I told her what had happened; but at first she thought I was rambling. Then I said, "There's a big woman sitting up in bed with her head wrapped in bandages; and she is knitting something with blue wool. She had a very red face." This certainly shook her; as apparently the lady concerned had a mastoid operation and was just as I described.

She was not allowed out of bed; and of course I hadn't been up at all. After several other details; such as the time by the clock on the wall, I convinced her that at least something strange had happened to me.

The OOBE has also been scientifically demonstrated. Dr. Charles Tart, a psychologist at the University of California at Davis, tested a young woman who could induce the OOBE habitually and reported his experiments in the *Journal of the American Society for Psychical Research* in 1968. The subject was placed in a dream laboratory room and was told to "float above her body," peer over a ledge situated above her, and remember and report back to him a multidigited number placed there for her to see. After a few days the subject alerted Tart over an intercom that she had had an out-of-the-body experience and correctly reported the number.

Out-of-the-body experiences indicate that an element of the mind, with cognitive and perhaps even physical capabilities, can exist beyond the confines of the body. There are even some cases on record during which the person undergoing on OOBE has been *seen as an apparition* by an observer. This should not seem peculiar, since many people who have had OOBEs perceived themselves as traveling in an apparitional-type body closely resembling their physical body. In 1973 I flew to Durham to carry out research with a gifted OOBE subject named Stuart "Blue" Harary, who can induce the experience at will. He was being tested at the Psychical Research Foundation. During the tests Blue would be situated in a Duke University laboratory and would be asked to "leave his body," travel half a mile to the PRF office buildings, and try to make animals housed there

The Poltergeist Experience

react to his presence. He was very successful at this task, and for an entire series of tests a kitten—which was normally very active and noisy—would immediately calm down and remain silent during the times Blue projected his mind to it. And during these tests some of the experimenters would see odd shadows darting about the room Blue was projecting to, or would experience strange internal feelings of his presence. One lab technician even saw Blue's apparition over a TV monitor. On the screen of a closed circuit TV set he saw Blue standing in a far corner of the room that was being monitored, and into which Blue was trying to send his mind for one of the experiments. Later he learned that this was exactly where Blue independently claimed he had been during the experiment. There can be little doubt that, whatever the OOBE is, some portion of the mind leaves the body and can make people and animals react to its visible or invisible presence.

What is this apparitional body? Is it a physical reality? This is a difficult question to resolve. On some occasions these bodies have been seen as apparitions by independent witnesses. However, they usually remain invisible to the human eye. Blue Harary seems to have a certain propensity for making his out-of-body presence known to those he visits. But not all people who have reported OOBEs describe being draped in an apparitional body. Blue, for instance, often perceives himself as a ball of light. (I once saw this ball of light, which greatly startled me!) At other times, he claims, he travels in a totally disembodied state but can create an apparitional body for himself at will. I have collected about thirty OOBE cases for my own files and although some of my correspondents report that they "left their bodies" and traveled about in an apparitional body, others report seeing themselves as mist, shafts, balls, or flames of light. There is, then, no one prototype for the OOBE.

Nonetheless there can be little doubt that during the OOBE some element of the mind physically detaches itself from the body and acts independently of it. However, the existence of an "astral body," which many people believe is projected during the experience, is an enigma, since not all out-of-the-body travelers experience it. This paradox has led Dr. Tart to suggest that the element of the mind which is released during the OOBE can fashion a replica of the human body for itself out of habit, even though this may not occur all the time. After all, we automatically perceive ourselves as having a body, so during the OOBE, suggests Tart, our out-of-the-body consciousness might therefore fashion a similar but artificial image in which to travel.

It also seems that this vehicle is quite capable of employing PK on occasion. Lucian Landau, an English student of parapsychology, reported one such experience which he shared with his wife, Eileen, who was a gifted out-of-the-body traveler. For the test Landau urged his wife to appear to him in her apparitional body and try to move an object telekinetically. The Landaus were occupying separate rooms that night and the experiment was quite successful. As Landau recorded in his report to the Society for Psychical Research:

I woke up suddenly, it was dawn, and there was just about enough light coming in through the curtains to enable me to read.... [There] stood the figure of Eileen, facing northwest, and looking straight ahead toward the window. The figure was wearing a night dress, its face was extremely pale, almost white.

The figure was moving slowly backwards toward the door, but it was otherwise motionless, it was not walking!...I got out of bed and followed. I could then clearly see the moving figure, which was quite opaque and looking like a living person, but for the extreme pallor of her face, and at the same time the head of Eileen, asleep in her bed and bedclothes rising and falling as she breathed. I followed the figure which moved all the time backwards, looking straight ahead, but apparently not seeing me. I kept my distance and ultimately stood in the door of a spare bedroom, when the figure...suddenly vanished. There was no visible effect on Eileen, who did not stir and whose rhythm of breathing remained unchanged. I moved quickly back to my room...and found a rubber toy dog, which belonged to Eileen which stood on a small chest of drawers.

The next morning Eileen recalled some of the previous night's out-of-the-body experience. She told her husband that she had awakened out-of-the-body and endeavored to carry out the suggested experiment.

"I lifted up my rubber toy dog," she writes, "and I remember taking it through the door, across the landing, to the other room but do not remember actually *walking*. I did not find the dog heavy or difficult to hold. I have no recollection of what I did with it."

The projection of a PK-imbued apparitional form could explain the apparitions seen in poltergeist cases and could possibly account for those instances in which objects appear to be "carried" or make odd flights; and the fact that a person can consciously project an apparition of himself capable of PK does not necessarily eliminate the possibility that he might also project this form *unconsciously*. There are a few cases on record in which people have had OOBEs during sleep, which they did not recall upon waking, even though their apparititions were seen miles away by startled onlookers. It is my opinion that certain aspects of these cases bear significantly on the nature of the poltergeist.

During poltergeist outbreaks, as in the OOBE, I believe that some element of the mind leaves the body and acts independently of it, and can also consolidate into a quasi-apparitional form. This lobotomized part of the mind (to use Fodor's phrase) is also capable of using PK to carry out such acts as throwing and otherwise transporting objects, banging on walls, setting fires, among other things. There is even some direct evidence for this theory. Mrs. Forbes reported many out-of-the-body experiences during the Thornton Heath poltergeist. In other cases, witnesses have noted that apparitions seen during the outbreak appear to *resemble* someone in the house.* The existence of the OOBE is a possible explanation for why the poltergeist seems to be both dependent and independent of the agent's unconscious mind simultaneously. But now, I would like to extend this idea even further.

During a poltergeist outbreak, the mind of the agent may be producing the phenomena by *especially* constructing a poltergeist-entity as its emissary. This poltergeist-entity, once it is released, probably develops a will of its own as it becomes only tenuously connected to the mind of the agent. There is some striking evidence that "mind forms" exist and can become animated. In fact, the production of mental beings (mental images so lifelike that even the producer cannot tell if they are genuine or not) is a very old yogic practice. And some of

* See my earlier book, *An Experience of Phantoms*, pp. 121-124, for a full discussion on this phenomenon.

these apparitions exhibit exactly the sort of intelligence witnessed during the poltergeist.

Probably the most famous description of a thought-form that took on a life of its own was reported by the late Alexandra David-Neel, a French woman who traveled to Tibet shortly after the turn of the century in order to study its culture and religion. A keen student of Tantric Buddhism, Mme. David-Neel soon became a practitioner of Tibetan yoga and was one of the very few Westerners ever to study directly under the lamas. She returned to France after her studies were completed and continued to practice Buddhism until her recent death. She was also one of the first Westerners to reveal the teachings and practices of the Tibetan yogis. (See her two outstanding books, *Magic and Mystery in Tibet* and *Initiates and Initiations in Tibet*.)

In her book *Magic and Mystery in Tibet,* Mme. David-Neel talks about the production of thought-forms and how they often take on lives of their own. She also describes her own experiment in producing one, and the nightmare that followed when what had begun as a purely mental image began to take on an independent life. For her experiment, Mme. David-Neel attempted to create the thought-form (or *tulpa*) of a short, fat, jolly monk. Her plan was to produce it so vividly that it would appear every bit as real and solid to her as anybody else. The following is her account of what happened:

I shut myself in *tsams* (in seclusion for meditation) and proceeded to perform the prescribed concentration of thought and other rites. After a few months the phantom monk was formed. His form grew gradually *fixed* and lifelike looking. He became a kind of guest, living in my apartment. I then broke my seclusion and started for a tour, with my servants and tents.

The monk included himself in the party. Though I lived in the open, riding on horseback for miles each day, the illusion persisted. I saw the fat *tulpa*, now and then it was not necessary for me to think of him to make him appear. The phantom performed various actions of the kind that are natural to travelers and that I had not commanded. For instance, he walked, stopped, looked around him. The illusion was mostly visual, but sometimes I felt as if a robe was lightly rubbing against me and once a hand seemed to touch my shoulder.

The features which I had imagined, when building my phantom, underwent a change. The fat, chubby-cheeked fellow grew leaner, his face assumed a vaguely mocking, sly, malignant look. He became more troublesome and bold. In brief, he escaped my control.

Once, a herdsman who brought me a present of butter saw the *tulpa* in my tent and took it for a live lama.

I ought to have let the phenomenon follow its course, but the presence of that unwanted companion began to prove trying to my nerves; it turned into a "day-nightmare." Moreover, I was beginning to plan my journey to Lhasa and needed a quiet brain devoid of other preoccupations, so I decided to dissolve the phantom. I succeeded, but only after six months of hard struggle. My mind creature was tenacious of life.

Mme. David-Neel's experience is not unique. Actually she included in her book many more fascinating accounts of how she witnessed the thought-forms of others. George Estabrooks, a well-known Harvard psychologist, went through a similar ordeal while experimenting with self-hypnosis. He successfully attempted to manufacture the hallucination of a polar bear through autosuggestion. Eventually he lost control of his mentally fabricated image and was soon terrified to discover that the bear-being would appear unsummoned. It would pop out at the startled psychologist from behind closed doors and from dark corners. Although Estabrooks's bear was probably a hallucinatory being, Mme. David-Neel's *tulpa* appears to have physically objectified, since other people were able to see it as well. What if her monk had been able to use PK or draw upon and use Mme. David-Neel's own innate PK potential?

Something very similar to this probably occurs during the poltergeist. Some split-off portion of the agent's mind directs the poltergeist by creating or becoming a visible or invisible PK-engendered *tulpa*, which perpetrates the poltergeistery. This splinter of the mind carries with it a will of its own. One might say that all of the agent's aggression, hate, guilt, and repression build into an artificial personality capable of leaving the body and acting independently of it. In the Type I (adolescent) poltergeist, this personality remains within the unconscious of the agent and works through his own mind. In the Type II entity-poltergeist, this detached part of the mind physically departs from the agent's mind and body and acts independent of it, drawing with it its own storehouse of PK, which it uses to produce the poltergeistery. This entity-poltergeist, a mass of projected PK, need not be produced by only one agent. A whole family might build up a collective external intelligence that can function independently of the group or any member of it. This entity-poltergeist intelligence might take a form and appear as an apparition just as the out-of-body consciousness can construct a human-like form for itself, or might remain as an intelligent mass of invisible PK. Thus Type I and Type II poltergeists are really two different aspects of the same phenomenon.

This theory can also explain why poltergeists

gradually subside. The "PK-being" must use the PK energy expended to create it to accomplish object-throwings and other manifestations. Therefore, in producing the poltergeistery, the entity also expends itself. I might also add that this "PK-being" theory does not rule out the possibility that somehow intelligences of the dead may activate some poltergeists, as Stevenson suggests. The PK-being may be sensitive to the influence of other external intelligence, or may be manipulated by the dead. Once an entity-poltergeist is projected, it may divide into several beings.

This theory is admittedly unconventional, but it does explain the greatest enigma of the poltergeist: how it can be associated with a living agent, yet show every sign of having its own intelligence. Actually, in my opinion a better idea of exactly what happens during a poltergeist outbreak is illustrated in an excellent science-fiction motion picture entitled *Forbidden Planet*. (Credit should go to the *Psychic* magazine's articles editor, Alan Vaughan, who was the first to cite the obvious parallel in print, but I would like to elaborate on it.) *Forbidden Planet* has a story line that exactly expresses what I think a poltergeist is.

A space crew crash-lands on a mysterious planet inhabited only by a hermit-like scientist and his daughter. The scientist is annoyed at this invasion. Soon the flight crew, who are trying desperately to restore their ship to working order, are besieged by mysterious attacks which kill and destroy. Finally the astronauts realize that they are being attacked by an invisible creature. The scientist who inhabits the planet is puzzled by the attacks until the flight commander (who has, of course, fallen in love with the scientist's daughter) discovers that the scientist is himself the unconscious culprit. Through a secret PK power he had stumbled upon, and which destroyed the planet's previous civilization, he had unconsciously acquired the ability to produce a PK-monster—a "Creature from the Id"—that carries out his secret desires. The scientist is stunned, since he realizes that he cannot control or stop the monster. Finally the monster attacks the scientist and his daughter only to be vanquished by the scientist's death.

Although the movie is pure fantasy, it is nonetheless true that every poltergeist attack represents a miniature *Forbidden Planet*. Each poltergeist agent is imbued with the ability to create a PK-being from his inner guilt, hate, and repression, which takes on a life of its own, knowing only that it exists to cause destruction. This creation grows in force until it completely severs itself from the will or personality that gave it birth. And it carries out its destruction until it loses its energy. If the PK-being remains closely connected to the agent's own mind, we have the minor type of poltergeist that disrupted the Miami warehouse or the Herrmann home in Seaford. If the entity-poltergeist can sever itself from the will of its creator, we have the horror that stalked and attacked Esther Cox, the Bell family, and possibly those poor souls attacked by demonic infestations and possession. The "Creatures from the Id" are more real than imaginary. And they are let loose in that amazing spectacle—the poltergeist.

8

Can We Overcome the Poltergeist?

A family persecuted by the poltergeist needs help. In fact, the one common bond uniting all the poltergeist victims chronicled in this book has been their desire to rid themselves of their unwelcomed guest. Just what can a family do if a poltergeist should erupt in their household? Can they do anything? Are there strategies they can use to battle the phenomena? Medical and psychological journals daily publish reams of material on preventive medicine, instructing people how to avert mental or physical ailments. Unfortunately parapsychology is not in such a position. We cannot instruct people how to avert psychic syndromes, nor have we any infallible methods of banishing the poltergeist once it strikes.

Few people realize how terrifying the poltergeist can be. I can remember being awakened early one morning by a telephone call from a frantic woman in Kentucky. In her haste to call, she had not considered that it was only 7 A.M. California time. She quickly told me that she heard banging noises on her stairway at night. Other people had heard them, too, she assured me. The sound of heavy footsteps, which seemed to walk up the stairs, stopping each night at her door, accompanied the raps. She was terrified and had called a local university, which had referred her to me.

In a situation like this there is painfully little one can do. I could not drop everything and fly to Kentucky to investigate the case, as I would have liked. I therefore gave the distraught woman as much assurance as I could that nothing harmful would happen to her and that the problem would soon be over. I advised her to keep active and simply to ignore the disturbance. Over the years I have found that this somewhat casual advice usually quiets things considerably. I have also found that more than anything else callers just want to talk with someone who will sympathize with them. In this particular case, I had no way of knowing whether or not there was a genuine poltergeist, but it made little difference. The woman was overwrought and calming her down was my immediate concern.

At 7 A.M. the next day the phone's ring seemed louder than the day before. It was the same woman, and she was just as frantic. The noises, she said, were worse. Over the years I have found that most people reporting disturbances do not call back after I have given them my advice, but it was apparent that in this case there was a definite problem at hand, so I told the woman to call W. G. Roll at the Psychical Research Foundation in Durham. I assured her that an investigator could be sent out from the lab, and that ended the conversation. I immediately phoned Bill Roll, reported the case to him, and told him to expect her call. Within thirty-six hours an investigator had been assigned to look into the matter and was dispatched to Kentucky. But it was too late. When the investigator arrived, he found that the woman had abandoned the house and could not be traced. Within only a few days this rather mild disturbance (in my opinion) had permanently driven her out of her house.

When a psychic investigator is called to the scene of a poltergeist, the family does not want measurements taken, their stories cross-examined, or to be grilled over and over about the incidents. They want help. But do we know enough about the poltergeist to be able really to help these people overcome these disturbances?

Since conventional poltergeists are so short-lived and abate rather rapidly, some experts believe that the poltergeist is not really a problem, but a cure within itself. That is, the poltergeist might act as a safety valve, blowing off the steam of repressed feelings. Unchecked and unexpressed (even unconsciously) these feelings might become mentally damaging to the victims. According to this view, the poltergeist's destructive acts actually cure and relieve the victim of feelings that could cause the person genuine mental illness unless expressed in some way. If one accepts this view, the emergence of a poltergeist is actually healthy.

Dr. John Layard, a Jungian psychologist in Great Britain, was the first to argue that the poltergeist was more the solution to a problem than a problem itself. (He presented this novel framework for understanding the poltergeist when he lectured before the Society for Psychical Research in 1944.) During the course of his private practice, Layard had come across a few instances of spontaneous PK which unquestionably had a therapeutic value for his patients. From these incidents he theorized that the poltergeist was simply a more dynamic manifestation of this same curative process. In each case, Layard argued, the PK had been instrumental in relieving unresolved tension. For example, one of his patients was harboring deep conflicts with his wife, whereas she presented a facade of cheerfulness to hide the fact that she was repressing her true feelings toward her husband. At the time of the PK incident the husband was in bed recovering from a concussion. A bell-ringing system had previously been installed so that he could summon his wife from downstairs when he needed her. One afternoon, while he was apparently fast asleep, the bells started to ring. His wife, who had come upstairs to answer, thought that her husband was only feigning sleep and was playing a joke on her. But when she asked if he had rung to request something, he could only mumble while semiconscious, "No, I was in a deep sleep, but my spirit is ringing. It is crying out." As soon as he said these words, the bells rang by themselves once again. The man soon awoke, but remembered nothing of the incident.

This incident symbolically represented the husband's need to express and resolve his conflict with his wife, Layard reasoned, and PK was his vehicle of expression. He was "summoning his wife," so to speak, to show his need to be close to her. In this case, therefore, the PK was used just as much to resolve a problem as to express it. Layard felt that interpreting PK as a form of nonverbal expression could have far-reaching implications. He believes that a psychologist trained to understand psychic phenomena may, by helping the victim also to understand the nature of PK, help or even cure him of his conflicts.

Layard only vaguely suggested that the poltergeist could be expelled by psychotherapeutic means. However, Nandor Fodor, who was also a clinician, actively attempted to "cure" a number of poltergeist victims, although he employed very different techniques. After investigating the Thornton Heath poltergeist (see chapter 2), Fodor became increasingly convinced that a psychodynamic process was at the heart of every outbreak. As a psychoanalyst, he believed that the poltergeist was a psychic mechanism which vented emotions locked within the confines of the agent's unconscious. The poltergeist represented to him something much deeper and more traumatic that simply denied hostility. But it was not until 1960, over twenty years after he encountered the Thornton Heath case, that he came to grips with this problem when trying to expel a poltergeist that was attacking a house in Baltimore.

The poltergeist was a fairly typical object-throwing type and centered on a seventeen-year-old science-fiction buff named Ted Pauls. (The boy's actual family name was Jones, but the teen-ager refused to use it.) The family had seen objects fall from shelves, bottles pop their caps or burst, and had watched other objects explode. In Fodor's view, the boy's preoccupation with science fiction was an escape mechanism, i.e., a desire to avoid dealing with practical responsibilities by yearning to return to the womb. This search for prenatal security was symbolized by the concept of a journey through space. (This was one of Ted's main preoccupations.) Ted was not an easy patient to handle; he was alarmed by the publicity the case had brought to his family and was hostile toward the press, which had become as much of a nuisance to him as the poltergeist. Fodor knew that to understand the poltergeist he had to get the young man's confidence.

"... the key to the mystery had to lie in the psyche of Ted Pauls," writes Fodor. "He was above the pubertal age but things had been happening in the house before, at Christmas time, for instance. Twice in the preceding year the decorative blue balls on the Christmas tree exploded with no known reason. I thought he must have a strong grievance against Christmas."

Fodor felt that, since Christmas is a birthday symbol, the boy's own birth had caused a trauma that was being relieved through the poltergeist.*

Fodor began his in-depth psychological evaluation of young Pauls by trying to find the motivation that might have engendered the poltergeist. His preliminary observations were disappointing: Ted's sexual development was normal; he had shown no history of passive hostility; and his interfamily relationship seemed no more difficult than any other teen-ager's. Only his total absorption with science fiction seemed peculiar. This interest had become an absolute obsession. At sixteen he had dropped out of school to devote yet more time to his hobby, and he was publishing a science-fiction newsletter he called *Fanjack*. It was through this hobby that the psychoanalyst finally found the solution to the case.

Fodor discovered that Pauls was not generally liked by his peers and had few friends. He had a funny walk, and youngish looks. These are all the type of characteristics teen-agers are often "ribbed" about. It was more than likely, thought Fodor, that Ted's problems in coping with his peers had caused him not only to find solace in science fiction but also eventually to leave school. In trying to determine how to abort the poltergeist, Fodor's first idea was to explain its nature to the boy, hoping that this

---

* Several psychologists, notably Otto Rank, have written about the concept of "birth trauma"; i.e., that one's physical birth can be a traumatic experience and might well affect the rest of one's life.

knowledge would prevent further manifestations from occurring. But he knew better. He knew that the boy would feel "accused" of causing the poltergeist, and that his aggression would probably be directed at himself, thus destroying the confidence he was so carefully trying to build. It might even aggravate the poltergeist. (I might add that I tried this "direct approach" in the James case and indeed it only made matters worse.) Fodor admitted in his clinical evaluation of the case:

I just did not know what to do, until out of the blue, a key was presented by the reading of a page of his editorial writing found in the cellar near the multigraphing machine. To my utter amazement I found that this young boy had a great talent for writing. At 17 he was an accomplished journalist. His vocabulary left nothing behind and his editorial handling of *Fanjack* showed a rare maturity. He was bursting with a rage for writing and no one in his immediate surroundings understood or appreciated him. They considered his pre-occupation nonsensical and drove against it with all their might. Was it, I queried, that the poltergeist activity arose from his creative rage?

Fodor theorized that Ted was fulfilling a need he had for creative expression through his science-fiction writing. It "elevated" him above his readers and helped to heal his crushed ego. Naturally, he assumed, if Ted received more acceptance by those around him and achieved greater self-confidence, the poltergeist activity would fade. Fodor took a gamble to prove his theory. Since he was not averse to publicity, he announced publicly on TV and radio that while investigating a poltergeist case he had uncovered a near literary genius. Fodor knew that this statement was not entirely truthful, but he thought that this sort of public acclaim might prove to be beneficial to Ted. It worked. The public esteem heaped upon Ted metamorphosed him. Suddenly his relatives appreciated his writing as a true talent and not as a disturbing obsession. They accepted him, congratulated him, and he was able to come out of the shell in which he had encased himself. He no longer had to be ashamed of himself for his writing.

This sudden change of attitude on the part of Ted and his relatives had a direct effect on the poltergeist. It abated through acceleration; that is, the outbreak suddenly became more violent and then gradually ceased altogether. (This type of intensification often occurs toward the end of some poltergeist outbreaks. It seems as if the poltergeist activates wildly as it tries to dissipate itself as quickly as possible. This is similar to a patient in analysis who will become very aggravated while "working through" a difficult problem.) To Fodor the case represented a new method of curing the victim of a poltergeist. Find the creative gift and lift the victim's ego by allowing his creativity to blossom, he urged.

Personally, I am not sure that Fodor actually discovered anything significant in his analysis of the Pauls case. Since poltergeists are capricious and extinguish themselves at almost any time, it is difficult to determine conclusively if his "therapy" really worked on Ted or simply coincided with the normal termination of the poltergeist. Fodor's cure also strikes me as too simple. I am forced to wonder if there is any evidence that Julio, Esther Cox, the Powhatan boy, or the neurotic Mrs. Forbes had any hidden creative gifts. Certainly there was no obvious evidence of it if one can judge from the reports on these cases.

On the other hand, any attempt to rechannel the force behind the poltergeist might be a fruitful method of alleviating the problem. A similar case to Fodor's Baltimore poltergeist has recently received considerable attention due to the fact that the principal protagonist, Matthew Manning, subsequently developed as a psychic and an artist. As in the Pauls case, Manning's poltergeistery ceased when he learned to redirect the force behind it.

As Manning relates in his book *The Link*, the poltergeist first made its appearance in February 1967. The Mannings were living in a relatively new house in England that year and there was no evidence that it was in any way "haunted." Matthew was eleven at the time. Derek Manning, the boy's father, was the first to realize that something peculiar was happening in the house. It all began when a silver tankard, which was kept on a wooden shelf in the living room, repeatedly fell to the floor. No one saw it move, but each morning it would be found displaced. Since none of the Manning children would confess to dislodging it, Mr. Manning placed talcum powder around the cup in the hope of determining which was the capricious child. The next morning the tankard was again on the floor but the powder was not disturbed. This indicated that the silver cup had risen *over* the powder before falling to the floor.

Soon the rest of the family noticed all sorts of peculiar phenomena in the house. Objects shifted position by themselves or were found in odd places. They usually moved only when no one was looking. Mr. Manning phoned the police but they, perhaps more enlightened than many police forces in the United States, suggested that he get in touch with the Cambridge Psychical

Research Society, whose secretary at the time was Dr. A. R. G. Owen, unfortunately, could give little advice on how to cure the poltergeist.

Meanwhile, happenings intensified. As Matthew Manning writes:

From the top of the stairs it was possible to hear knocks and other sounds as the upheavals increased, but we did not witness any of these objects in flight. Invariably the objects moved were lightweight ornaments, chairs, cutlery, ashtrays, baskets, plates, a small coffee table and a score of other articles, but none was ever broken or spilled. The tankard was regularly moved; we wondered if it was perhaps some form of defiant protest against my father, since it was his tankard, and he alone drank from it....

As the physical manifestations increased, the house began to produce erratic and unsuspected taps and creaks. The noises would vary from a dull knocking to a sound like small stones being thrown at the window, and they continued throughout the day and night in all parts of the house.

By this time, Owen had arrived on the scene. He and Derek Manning patrolled the house, hoping to witness the PK activity but none occurred in their presence. As soon as they were distracted or left the living room, however, objects would be found displaced. Owen even attempted to outwit the poltergeist by hiding his car some distance away and "sneaking" into the house early one morning in order to observe the living room while the household was still asleep. But the entity-poltergeist was wary. Once again nothing happened while Owen watched the room, but objects moved about as soon as he left his post.

The elder Manning eventually sent his three children off to relatives to see if their absence would eliminate the poltergeist. The plan was logical, for by this time Dr. Owen had advised him about the connection between the poltergeist and adolescent children. And just as Owen expected, the PK ceased. However, more active poltergeistery resulted upon Matthew's return home. Now for the first time large objects were shoved about or tipped over. As Matthew humorously observed, it was as though the poltergeist had to "make up for lost time." The height of the demonstrations took place the day after Matthew Manning came home. PK manifestations occurred in rapid succession, but from that day on the phenomena lost force. But the poltergeist was hardly over.

About a year later, while at boarding school, Matthew developed a renewed interest in psychic phenomena. Ouija-board séances had become a craze, and the excited youth joined in the fun wholeheartedly. He knew, though, that many of his friends were "cheating" and manually moving the Ouija-board pointer. Nonetheless, Matthew's years at school were quiet, despite his toying with the occult. The poltergeist was more of a dim recollection than a vivid memory when, during one of his vacations at home in 1970, the poltergeist seemed to be reactivating. Cupboard doors opened by themselves and other minor manifestations harassed the Mannings. But the PK always stopped when Matthew returned to school.

Christmas 1970 initiated the poltergeist's full reappearance when Matthew awoke to hear scratching noises emanating from behind the wood that paneled his room. Strange footsteps outside his window followed.

Later, pillows were thrown at him. School was his haven after these outbreaks, since only there was he protected from the poltergeist's activity. But gradually it became active there as well. Soon there was a full repetition of the 1967 outbreak at the Manning home, but this time the poltergeist was more powerful.

I had gone to bed . . . and I lay there restlessly although I do not remember whether it was particularly hot that night [writes Manning, who had just returned home]. I suddenly heard a scraping noise coming from the direction of the cupboard, which continued for almost thirty seconds. Having listened to it for a moment, I switched on my lamp and saw to my horror that the cupboard was inching out from the wall toward me. When it halted it had advanced about eighteen inches. I switched off the light and almost simultaneously my bed started to vibrate violently back and forth. I was now too timid to move and I lay in anticipation of whatever might happen next. The vibrating ceased and I felt the bottom end of my bed rising from the floor to what I estimated to be about one foot. The head of the bed then rose two or three inches, and the same time the bed pitched out toward the center of the room and finally settled at an angle to the wall.

The experience was unnerving to say the least, so Matthew retreated to his parents' room where he bedded down in a sleeping-bag on the floor. The night passed peacefully. But the next morning:

The first room we saw was the dining room. It looked as though a bomb had hit it. Chairs were upturned or simply not in the room, the table was no longer on its feet, and ornaments were strewn around the room and on the floor. The sitting room was in a similar state as was nearly every other ground floor room in the house. Table and chairs were piled on top of each other, pictures were dismounted, and several objects and pieces of cutlery had vanished.

This situation was repeated over the next several days as new phenomena were added to the poltergeist's activities. Objects were found delicately balanced on each other; electrical appliances malfunctioned; childish scrawlings defaced the walls; and pools of water materialized on the floors all over the house. By this time the family actually saw objects as they were thrown or rattled about. It was not unusual for small objects to fly at odd trajectories, even making 90-degree turns in flight. Reminiscent of the Esther Cox poltergeist, the words "Matthew Beware" were scribbled on a wall at the height of the violence. The poltergeist had now taken on definite intelligence and was carrying out motivated acts. For example, the Mannings could request that a specific object be moved to a designated location and the poltergeist would often comply.

Actually, I believe that the Manning case represents the evolution of a Type II poltergeist from a Type I poltergeist. At the outset the epidemic was mild. The 1967 manifestations were extremely so, but by 1971 the poltergeist was carrying out willful acts such as writing, obeying commands, and destroying houseware. I believe that Matthew may have created an entity-poltergeist of a force and independence that he failed to achieve during the earlier outbreak.

This time, however, the poltergeist followed Matthew back to school, much to the excitement of his schoolmates and to the chagrin of the headmaster. Had it not been for the wise counseling of Owen (who had emigrated to Canada by this time but who was following the case through correspondence), Matthew might have been expelled. Although at first only his room was plagued by the poltergeistery, the PK soon broke out in other rooms in the dormitory. Pools of water material-ized on the floors, bookcases overturned, and furniture was displaced. But, in spite of these violent displays, the poltergeist seemed more eager to intimidate than do bodily harm. Matthew reported:

On many occasions, when we were all in bed, objects would hurtle toward somebody, as if to strike the person, and then either swing away at an angle, just before he was hit, or strike him so lightly that it was hardly felt. Hurtling objects missed people literally by a few inches and often hit the wall behind their heads.

One witness to the proceedings, a matron at the school, also observed stone-throwings. She writes:

In my sitting room I might be sitting quietly perhaps sewing, sometimes listening to the wireless, when I am suddenly soaked with coldness, and a shower of pebbles falls from the ceiling. Some nights it may be little chippings of wood which drop into my lap.

During this final phase of the violence Matthew discovered a way to redirect the force behind the poltergeist. His discovery closely resembled that which Fodor made in his analysis of the Baltimore case: Matthew began developing a talent for automatic writing. First came communications from personalities claiming to be the dead, but more artistic gifts soon became apparent. Although Manning had little formal art training, he developed through automatic writing the ability to produce delicate and beautifully executed drawings. The gradual refinement of the automatic writing and drawing slowed the poltergeist down, and it finally disappeared altogether as the writings became Manning's vehicle for self-expression.

What is all this telling us about the poltergeist? There are two very different ways we can interpret Matthew's newfound talents. One is that they were further manifestations and developments of his psychic ability; in other words, the writings really were from the dead or represented a psychic process at work. Since his drawings were of a quality apparently beyond his normal skills, perhaps this talent was also being directed by some outside agency such as spirits of the dead.

On the other hand, even if his scripts did show evidence of ESP-based information, we can still interpret the automatic writing as a means Matthew used to release subconscious creative expression. As Dr. Anita Mühl reported in her excellent book *Automatic Writing*, even if nothing paranormal comes out of automatic writing, the very ability to produce such scripts reveals the possible presence of a vast amount of repressed creativity that can blossom through practice. In fact, one recently deceased California psychologist taught automatic writing to his patients (since many people can develop the technique) in order to help these individuals get a more accurate picture of their inner abilities and feelings.

This is certainly true of Manning's drawings. Exquisitely styled and beautifully rendered, they represent the working of Matthew's own inner creativity, which had finally found a proper outlet.

Matthew himself has conflicting attitudes about his

talents. When I first met him in 1975 he quite frankly admitted to me that he had no way of telling if his automatic writing and artistic productions were a psychic or a psychological phenomenon, nor could he calculate what percentage of them stemmed from his own mind or to what extent paranormal influences guided him. He did feel that some of his automatic writing was inspired by the dead, but calculated these scripts as accounting for only 5 percent of the whole.

Matthew also developed as a gifted psychic during this period of his life, and began to develop ESP abilities. After watching the renowned Israeli psychic Uri Geller on television, Matthew also developed the ability to bend metal objects by PK. These PK abilities were subsequently tested experimentally by Dr. A. R. G. Owen and his colleagues at the New Horizons Foundation in Canada.*

The Manning case is in some ways unique, however. Rarely do poltergeist victims become psychics after the outbreak has ended. Usually the PK becomes completely dormant. Although Hans Bender has found that some poltergeist agents are gifted with exceptional ESP ability, it is astonishing how few of them ever learn to control their PK talents. Matthew is one of the few who has. He was able to overcome the poltergeist by developing both his creative and his psychic abilities. Harnessing and redirecting them seemed to rechannel the poltergeist completely, vanquishing it at the same time. I am sure that Nandor Fodor, were he alive today, would point to Matthew with great satisfaction. For, as he prophesied in his report on the Baltimore poltergeist:

---

* See A.R.G. Owen, "A Preliminary Report on Matthew Manning's Physical Phenomena," *New Horizons* 1 (1974): 171-172.

Find the frustrated creative gift, lift up a crushed ego, give love and confidence and the poltergeist will cease to be. After that you can proceed with psychoanalysis, release the unconscious conflicts, but whether you do it or not, a creative self-expression will result in a miraculous transformation.

You might be wondering by now why parapsychologists have not tried to harness and direct the poltergeist force by helping the agent unfold his psychic potentials. The answer is simple. They have, but these attempts have usually been absolute fiascos, as the endeavors of one investigator, J. Hewat McKenzie, so embarrassingly reveal.

McKenzie was one of the greatest Spiritualists of his day. A businessman, he acquired a sizable personal fortune, which he used to organize his London-based British College of Psychic Science in 1920. (This now defunct organization has no connection with the present College of Psychic Studies, also in London.) The college was founded as a center for psychics. Here they could come to be tested and trained and then offer their professional services. However, McKenzie also wanted his college to be a research center where individuals and investigators could experiment with both physical and mental mediums. Although not a psychic himself, he was one of those rare people who had the ability to nurture the psychic abilities of those who came to him. His gift for helping others understand, control, and unfold their talents allowed him the opportunity to develop and work with some of the greatest psychics of the time. The late Eileen Garrett was perhaps the most gifted and famous medium of the 1940s, and her talents were nurtured by McKenzie at his college.

McKenzie believed that an active poltergeist could be

aborted by teaching the agent to use and control his PK. For years he attempted to prove his theory, but finally gave up when his logical plan repeatedly failed. When the agents were placed in a situation where they were expected to produce PK, their abilities invariably vanished. In one case, McKenzie was called in to investigate a poltergeist that was disrupting a woolen mill in Yorkshire, where machinery constantly broke down in the presence of a twenty-year-old girl. (She was called only Miss G. in his report.) At home, ornaments dislodged from the fireplace and china shattered. The damage eventually became so extensive that Miss G. was served with an eviction notice by her landlord. Whether it was due to psychological strain or to the poltergeist, Miss G. began having fainting spells and was confined to a hospital. Although epilepsy was at first suspected, she was soon discharged and went back to work at the factory. The next three days at the factory were tumultuous as urns overturned, tables slid across the floor, and other objects flew about.

Fortunately the factory manager was familiar with psychic studies, and he called in McKenzie to investigate. Upon arriving on the scene, McKenzie accompanied by his secretary, Muriel Hankey, tried to channel the girl's ability by organizing an impromptu seance. The factory lights were dimmed and McKenzie, Muriel Hankey, and Miss G. sat at a small table. It immediately began to move. At first McKenzie thought the girl might be turned into a gifted psychic, so he took her with him to the British College of Psychic Science for further development. Unfortunately the poltergeist continued despite all McKenzie's attempts to rechannel it. McKenzie estimated that the girl's presence at the college caused over $100 worth of damage in breakage, and although nothing at all occurred when Miss G. tried consciously to produce PK, the poltergeist activity flared even when the girl engaged in purely domestic activities. As McKenzie noted:

> G. was on her knees wiping the linoleum, and the housemaid was dusting. A large and heavy carved armchair turned round and went quietly on its side on the floor, about 4 feet from G. A few minutes later the housekeeper saw another armchair (slightly lighter) turn around and do the same, G. still on her knees, 5 feet away.
>
> A gas stove...awaiting removal...stood in the corridor, with ½ cwt. of heavy stove fittings and trays securely placed on top. The girl had just passed this when the whole of these fittings fell on the floor.

Sometimes the PK would become exceptionally active. Moments after Miss G. was shown to bed one night by Mrs. McKenzie, her room looked "as if a tornado had swept over it."

Miss G. was only one of the many poltergeist victims McKenzie tried to cure during his career. Finally he realized that the generally young ages of the victims, the basically spontaneous nature of poltergeistic PK, and the difficulty in controlling PK all worked against his endeavors to turn these victims into mediums. He worked with one girl on a case for an entire year, but he was never successful, and finally abandoned the idea that the poltergeist could be controlled.

Why can't we overcome the poltergeist by developing the agent's psychic abilities? The answer may lie in the fact that PK is a power that is "ego-alien." That is, it is so foreign to our normal way of looking at the world, and especially at ourselves, that we refuse to take responsibility for PK when it occurs. Our natural tendency is to blame someone else for the phenomenon. It is perhaps for this reason that spirits or demons are usually blamed when the poltergeist erupts. This view has been espoused by Dr. Rex Stanford, a psychologist who was until recently engaged in parapsychological research at St. John's University in New York. Stanford points out that mediums usually ascribe their PK powers to spirits of the dead working through them. Likewise, spirits, demons, and elementals are all generally blamed for the poltergeist when it occurs. (In some eight years of active investigation I have never come across any case, genuine or not, in which the family did not blame demons or spirits for the activity.) Stanford believes that this tendency is a natural psychological reaction, in that it keeps the victim from having to take personal responsibility for the PK. Poltergeist effects also usually occur when everyone is distracted. This, too, may be an indication of the ego-alien nature of PK; i.e., the agent only projects the PK—or at least only activates it unconsciously—at those specific times when his conscious mind is preoccupied.

If Stanford's views are correct, the séance setting would be the *worst* place to try to control the PK. During the séance the agent becomes the focus of attention; he is held responsible for the PK, and his full attention is directed toward the phenomena. However, during a poltergeist attack there usually are enough people about that this "ownership" inhibition is minimal. The poltergeist can erupt and the agent can plead total nonresponsibility and be believed—at least at first. It does not seem likely, therefore, that we can overcome the poltergeist by training the agent to use his PK creatively or under controlled conditions. The case of Matthew Manning is a rare exception to this general rule.

Since the poltergeist represents a psychological as well as a psychic problem, can we overcome it by clinically counseling the afflicted family or the agent? In other words, can we give the poltergeist psychotherapy? W. G. Roll's discoveries have helped substantiate the theory that the conventional poltergeist evolves when its agent can no longer deal with pent-up hostility. As with so many other psychological problems, the poltergeist might represent more of a total family disturbance than a personal problem unique to the agent. For example, we might ask: What type of relationships exist within a family which would prohibit the agent from expressing his hostilities in a normal verbal or physical manner? When treating a mental problem many clinical psychologists have found it more fruitful to concentrate on the family as a unit than on the individual. (See, for example, C. F. Midelfort's *The Family in Psychotherapy*.) We might adopt this same approach when attempting to treat the poltergeist. After all, a psychical researcher has several responsibilities when he investigates a poltergeist. Not only has he a responsibility to investigate properly the alleged occurrences and do what he can in terms of research and observation, but he also has a duty to help the family understand what is actually happening to them. He must also try to get to the psychological root of the problem and, to the best of his ability, do all he can to "cure" it.

There can be little doubt that in most poltergeist cases the agent's repressed anger is usually directed at such emotionally binding targets as parents and guardians.

This setting is also a classical breeding ground for the emergence of mental illness. Gregory Bateson, a noted psychologically oriented anthropologist, has developed what he calls the "double-bind" theory to explain schizophrenia. According to this theory, schizophrenia is not due to a problem unique to the patient, but is a breakdown that occurs when the patient receives contradictory messages from people who are emotionally important to him. For instance, a mother might demand affection from her daughter but act coldly toward her when she does bestow it. Bateson argues that a total breakdown results when a person continually receives contradictory demands such as these.

The poltergeist, too, represents an interpersonal problem. It is not a coincidence that poltergeists usually emerge within a family setting. Poltergeists *do* represent a form of expression. And the fact that it shows motivation and intelligence has also been substantiated by two psychologists who have been able to watch poltergeist activity in their offices while they were giving therapy to the agents.

The first of these cases was was reported by Mary Williams, a Jungian analyst, who witnessed the PK while treating a thirty-two-year-old man named Roger, who was recovering from a psychotic breakdown. Roger claimed that he was being persecuted by a poltergeist, a claim that Mrs. Williams apparently did not take seriously at first. But she revised her opinion when raps and other PK phenomena occurred during their therapy sessions. Mrs. Williams gradually came to realize that these outbreaks were not random occurrences, but occurred only when the patient's hostility turned toward her as therapist.

A similar case was reported by Elwood Worcester, a forgotten pioneer of psychical research who sought to combine medicine, religion, and later psychic studies in treating the "whole man." Worcester was attempting to cure a drug addict who believed herself "possessed" by the spirit of a deceased doctor. As he questioned her during therapy while trying to establish the cause of her problem, the patient went into a trance and raps were heard in the room. Again it appeared as if the PK were a symbolic protest against the therapist's probings.

In both cases the poltergeist PK was used as a means of psychological expression. This is the same type of protest the agents are making during conventional poltergeist disturbances; but in these cases the hostility is directed at the family. If we can determine what exactly the poltergeist is trying to express, then we should be able to overcome it by resolving the conflict that has forced the PK into the open. I was actually able to test this theory in 1973 when a poltergeist report was turned over to me from the University of California at Los Angeles (UCLA). I went to the afflicted house that same day and returned again later that evening with Raymond Bayless.

The members of the Roman Catholic family, whom I will call the Carters,* included Mr. Carter, a South American–born industrial engineer, his American wife, and their five children: Carol (aged seventeen), Sharon (sixteen), Stan (fourteen), Mark (thirteen), and Pauline (eleven). They had been living in their four-bedroom, upper-middle-class home for thirteen years. Unfortu-

---

* I gave a brief synopsis of this case in my earlier book *An Experience of Phantoms*, but did not go into the psychological dynamics of the poltergeist.

nately we were not able to witness any of the poltergeist
activity at the house, but the evidence in the case was
strong, since none of the testimony we collected was
contradictory, and there was at least one outside witness
to the disturbances.

The first incident occurred in November 1972, when
Pauline noticed that a small stuffed dog she kept in her
room was behaving oddly. For one thing, one of its big
floppy ears started to move up and down by itself. Two
weeks later, Sharon and Pauline were talking in the
bedroom and Pauline was holding the little stuffed
animal when it suddenly flew out of her hands and struck
the wall adjacent to the bed upon which she was lying.
Both girls witnessed this occurrence, but it wasn't until
January that the outbreak intensified.

During this time several members of the family began
hearing breathing sounds and footsteps throughout the
house, and once Mrs. Carter felt a mysterious cold breeze
on her face. Two nights before I was called to the scene,
Carol heard footsteps and breathing in the hallway, and
at first thought there was a burglar in the house. Finally
she got up to investigate and although she saw nothing,
she continued to hear the breathing sounds. She became
frightened and woke her mother. Mrs. Carter verified the
incident but she did not hear the noises herself. Both Stan
and Mark, though, reported hearing similar sounds that
night.

Mrs. Carter had her own experience to relate. She told
us that once while she was doing her morning chores and
while the children were still asleep, her portable radio
switched stations and volume by itself. She readjusted the
set but the same thing happened as soon as she turned
her back. Sharon reported a similar tug-of-wills over the

radio, and claimed that she had seen the dials on the set move by themselves. The radio was a focal point for the poltergeist in this case. It would switch positions and turn on and off by itself. These incidents were witnessed by many members of the family.

The poltergeist had escalated the night before our arrival. Mark had seen a shadow-like form in his room, which he thought was that of a burglar. His suspicions grew when he heard shuffling sounds from his sister's room (which adjoined his) soon after the figure had departed. A similar shadow was reported by Stan. The denouement to this strange drama took place the next morning when Sharon glanced into her closet. Her clothes were in disarray, and several hangers were propped outward at a 45-degree angle instead of hanging normally. No one in the family had moved them and they were shown to me still propped in their curious position when I first visited the house. All hangers without clothes on them had been altered, and it was a rather bizarre sight.

The apparitions started to appear the morning after when Sharon and Carol both saw what they could only describe as "apparitional feet" in the hallway. Mrs. Carter was also in the hallway, but all she reported seeing was an amorphous shape. Carol became agitated at the invasion, grabbed a crucifix, and demanded that the entity leave. Her outbreak quieted things considerably, but shortly afterward came the event which sparked the family to call UCLA.

The activity began again a few hours later when Mark was with Pauline in his bedroom listening to the radio. This time the volume control on the set was suddenly turned up. The family became so frightened by this event that all the children huddled into the master bedroom with their mother. When the radio stopped playing an instant later, the family discovered that its plug had been pulled out from the wall. Everyone who witnessed the incident confirmed the story. They had all been in each other's company, so no one could have faked the incident. Soon after, a relative of Mrs. Carter's called UCLA.

I first spoke to Mrs. Carter on the telephone at 11:45 that morning and I made an appointment to see the family at 1 o'clock. During the interim two odd events allegedly took place. As Sharon told me later, she and Mark were playing chess when they smelled the distinct odor of after-shave lotion. Upon investigating, she found an open bottle of their father's lotion in the bathroom. (After Sharon recounted this story to us, Mr. Carter added that he is compulsive about putting caps back on bottles, and further told us that he had not used the lotion that day.) Shortly after, the toilet seemed to flush inexplicably when no one was in the bathroom. Furthermore the top of the toilet tank had been displaced.

When the family members had enumerated all the manifestations they could recall, we discussed the incidents with them in order to determine how they felt about them. We explained a little about the dynamics and nature of RSPK phenomena and gave them some advice about how to handle the situation.

The most effective way of handling this situation was to get the family discussing the odd events and talking them over with one another and with us. We wanted to help them understand the etiology of the poltergeist, and to view it as one of many means of expression, while siphoning out any thought that the disturbances were "supernatural." We discussed the nature of family tensions and explained how the poltergeist emerges when normal expression becomes blocked. Of course, we "blamed" no one for the problem, nor did we point out any likely poltergeist agent. Instead we urged them to accept the explanation that *as a family* they were creating the poltergeist to express some sort of group frustration.

This technique and procedure is not a new one in clinical psychology; in fact, it is a modified form of a system of psychotherapy developed by Benjamin Karpman. The key to his system is to help the patient understand the nature of his own psychological problem (see Karpman's *Objective Therapy*). Hopefully, once this is achieved the problem will begin to cure itself. Karpman also suggests what he calls "bibliotherapy," in which the patient is assigned reading material concerning his problem to help him achieve this insight. For instance, if the patient is suffering from neurotic depression, he would be asked to read a number of books or articles on the nature of depression.

This type of insight will sometimes help a person to handle psychic experiences which he does not understand or has found anxiety-provoking. For example, several years ago I was approached by a clinical psychologist and friend who was having difficulty treating a female patient. The patient had reported precognitive dreams about car accidents and had falsely blamed herself for them when the accidents actually occurred. The therapist was at a loss to handle the case. I suggested that the woman be given assigned readings on parapsychology and especially on precognition. I also urged my friend to reassure her constantly that such dreams are very common occurrences. It was important to make her aware that there was nothing wrong with having psychic experiences; that hundreds of people report them; that it in no way represents a "problem" in itself; and that in fact they can be richly rewarding experiences. The psychologist took the advice and the woman improved considerably within a few weeks.

I use a similar approach when aiding poltergeist victims. Raymond Bayless and I talked to the Carters about the nature of the poltergeist experience so that they could begin to achieve some insight into their problem. However, this is only a first step in dealing with a victimized family, for while perhaps momentarily stopping the poltergeist it will not necessarily terminate it. To vanquish the poltergeist, the hidden hostilities and repression at the root of the problem must be verbalized and safely expressed. If these conflicts can be aired openly, thus relieving the tension, the poltergeist has no need to strike.

While "poltergeist agents" are undoubtedly responsible for many cases, some poltergeists are generated by the total family. There seemed to be no specific agent in the Carter case, even though much of the activity centered around Sharon. Most of the members had witnessed occurrences independently of the others, and Mrs. Carter had observed the PK when no one else was present in the house or when they were asleep. There was nothing to indicate that any specific member of the family was disturbed. They all seemed amiable, fascinated by but fearful of the poltergeist, and collectively catalyzed a rather mild Type II poltergeist. While talking with the family the evening of my second visit, I secretly hoped that if the Carters could discuss their frustrations openly and unashamedly, the poltergeist could be banished. I started to manipulate the conversation in this direction and, happily for all of us, the family seemed to be aware of where my line of questioning was leading and gave us the clue to what I feel was the root cause of the outbreak.

It became apparent during this discussion that the family members were less than happy in their home. Mr. Carter was Brazilian-born and in the past had taken his family on visits to Mexico and Brazil. The entire family very much wished to leave Los Angeles and take up residence in one of the South American countries. Unfortunately Mr. Carter's efforts to get a transfer of his job failed. He admitted feeling frustrated and his family, one by one, conceded that they too were disheartened by the situation.

To my mind the pent-up emotions involved in this checkmated position released the poltergeist. Feelings of hostility and frustration were common to the entire family. What's more, there was no real method by which they could work out these feelings normally. There was no one to "strike out" at. So I believe that the family invoked a poltergeist to relieve the tension and symbolically attack the house, which they wanted to leave. After the family got all their frustrations out into the open I knew the poltergeist was over. It was, and never bothered the Carters again for the years I have kept in touch with them.

The Carters were an extremely intelligent family, and one to whom the poltergeist was a challenge as well as a threat. It is no wonder, then, that we were able to alleviate their problem. However, this case was extremely mild in comparison to that of the Bell family or the nineteenth-century Amherst incidents.

When dealing with mild outbreaks, I see no reason why the poltergeist cannot be overcome by working therapeutically with the family. But some poltergeists are so vicious, and the family setting so disturbed that, like a rampaging fire, the best solution might be to let the poltergeist fade of its own accord. One psychoanalyst I know visited a family in the Midwest which had long been plagued by a poltergeist. He left after a short stay, and told his colleagues that the family relationships were so unnatural that it was beyond his psychiatric ability to help them work out their personal difficulties, much less their psychical ones.

The poltergeist, since it has intelligence, might also have an instinct for self-preservation. It, too, might have the ability to strike out when threatened. The fact that poltergeists often accelerate before terminating might be due not only to the PK exhausting itself quickly, but also to an abortive method the poltergeist is using to fight against its ultimate extinction. As I stated earlier, confronting the poltergeist is just as much a battle as it is an exploration. Who will eventually win the battle? We need to know a great deal more about the poltergeist before we will be in a position to suggest a sure-fire way to vanquish the poltergeist.

Epilogue

The poltergeist provides us with only a glimmer of a psychic world which lies far beyond the access of our normal minds and senses. Apparitions, hauntings, telepathy, and clairvoyance are all phenomena and faculties which, like the poltergeist, continually shed new light on the hidden dimensions of our minds.

It is hard to approach any topic concerning psychic phenomena without moralizing about it. Almost every book on ESP includes some optimistic notes about how psychic abilities are either atavistic powers lost to modern mechanistic man or a forerunner of a supersense soon to revolutionize him. Few books on psychic phenomena end without pointing out that ESP is something good, transcendent, even godly. Books on hauntings and apparitions usually end by comforting the reader with the fact that these experiences assure man of his ultimate mastery over nature—personal immortality.

Man habitually romanticizes his hidden powers. Perhaps this is a defense against our innate fear of the unknown. Healing powers and the evolution of consciousness are all promises held out by the study of PK. But are these hopes valid or are they merely fantasies?

`I cannot look upon man's psychic potential so lovingly. There is nothing angelic about it, nor demonic. Like intelligence, personality, needs and goals, our psychic faculties are a normal part of our biological and psychological constitution. They should only excite our awe because their manifestations are so mysterious to us, and not because they represent anything supernatural.

The poltergeist represents the "dark side of the soul." Psychic ability can be just as destructive and wicked as it is altruistic. I hope I have made it clear in this survey that the poltergeist is a terrible force. There can be nothing less spiritual than the poltergeist while on its rampage. ESP and PK are not harbingers of a new spirituality or a prelude to man's evolution into superman. Psi is nothing more than a basic component of our mind, which for over the few thousand years of recorded history has never ceased to amaze man when it is manifested. I doubt that its status as an anomaly will change in the future. It can just as easily be used to vent man's primitive urges and hostilities as it can be used to help him.

In thinking about man's unwelcomed guest, the poltergeist, let us remember that our psychic abilities can plague as well as benefit us.

References

1. THE HIDDEN FORCES OF THE MIND

The research with Felicia Parise is described in a symposium "Psychokinesis on Stable Systems: Work in Progress," in W. G. Roll, R. L. Morris, and J. D. Morris (eds.), *Research in Parapsychology, 1973* (Metuchen, N.J.: Scarecrow Press, 1974). The cases from Camille Flammarion are taken from his three-volume work *Death and Its Mysteries* (New York: Century, 1921–1923). Jung's cases appear in his own *Memories, Dreams, Reflections* (New York: Vintage Books, 1961).

2. THE UNNATURAL HISTORY OF THE POLTERGEIST

The Perrault case may be found in Herbert Thurston's *Ghosts and Poltergeists* (Chicago: Gateway, 1954). The Wesley poltergeist appears in Harry Price's *Poltergeist over England* (London: Country Life, 1945), which reproduces the original letters and reports, and the Bell Witch was originally reported in an old book by W. V. Ingram, *Authenticated History of the Bell Witch* (reprinted, Nashville, Tenn.: Rare Book Reprints, 1961). Bell-ringing poltergeists, including the Bealings Bells, are recapped in Rupert T. Gould's *Enigmas* (London: Geoffrey Bles, 1929). The Fox case can be found in any history of psychical research and in detail in Alan Gauld's *The Founders of Psychical Research* (New York: Schocken Books, 1968). Barrett's observations are included in his paper "Poltergeists—Old and New," *Proceedings of the Society for Psychical Research* 25 (1911). Lombroso's Turin case was included in his own book, *After Death—What?* (Boston: Small, Maynard & Co., 1909). Podmore's material is from a paper, "Poltergeists," *Proceedings of the Society for Psychical Research* 12 (1896). The Swedish case was written up in a paper, "Karin: An Experimental Study of Spontaneous Rappings," by Hjalmar Wijk, in *Annals of Psychical Science* 2 (1905). The case of Eleanore Zugun appears in Price's *Poltergeist over England* (cited above) and in his *Leaves from a Psychist's Case Book* (London: Gollancz, 1933). The Thornton Heath poltergeist and Fodor's views on the poltergeist are set forth in his *On the Trail of the Poltergeist* (New York: Citadel, 1958), and also in Hereward Carrington and Nandor Fodor's *Haunted People* (New York: E. P. Dutton, 1951).

3.   THE RAMPAGING MIND

All of W. G. Roll's cases appeared in lengthy papers in the *Journal of the American Society for Psychical Research* except for the Seaford account, which appeared in the *Journal of Parapsychology*. These cases are incorporated into his book, *The Poltergeist* (New York: New American Library, 1973), which cites the original papers and gives in-depth consideration to the Seaford, Miami, and Olive Hill poltergeists. The Sauchie case was published in A. R. G. Owen, *Can We Explain the Poltergeist?* (New York: Garrett Publications/Helix Press, 1964). The Powhatan case can be found as a paper, "A Case of RSPK Involving a Ten Year Old Boy: The Powhatan Poltergeist," by John Palmer, in *Journal of the American Society for Psychical Research* 68 (1974): 1-33. Hans Bender's poltergeist investigations were given in his presidential address to the Parapsychological Association, "New Development in Poltergeist Research," *Proceedings of the Parapsychological Association* 5 (1968): 29-38, which includes John Mischo's paper, "Personality Structure of Psychokinetic Mediums." For Cox's comparative analysis of the poltergeist, see "Introductory Comparative Analysis of Some Poltergeist Cases," *Journal of the American Society for Psychical Research* 55 (1961): 47-72. Richardson's analysis of temperature change and the poltergeist can be found in Harry Price, *Poltergeist over England* (cited above), and Schmeidler's PK tests with Ingo Swann were published as "PK Effects upon Continuously Recorded Temperature," *Journal of the American Society for Psychical Research* 67 (1973): 325-340. Harry Price's tests with Stella C. are included in his book, *Stella C.* (London: Hurst & Blackett Ltd., 1925). The Oakland case is recounted in J. Gaither Pratt, *ESP Research Today* (Metuchen, N.J.: Scarecrow Press, 1973).

4. STONE-THROWING ATTACKS

The Sumatra case was published in the *Journal of the Society for Psychical Research* XII: 260-266, while

Sanderson's observations were included in W. G. Roll's *The Poltergeist* (cited above). The historical data on stone-throwing poltergeists are drawn from H. Carrington and N. Fodor's *Haunted People* (cited above), and the case witnessed by M. Laval is reported in Camille Flammarion's *Haunted Houses* (New York: D. Appleton & Co., 1924). A complete report on the Woodroffe case is presented in Herbert Thurston's *Ghosts and Poltergeists* (cited above). Additional data on the Big Bear and Lynwood cases are given in Bayless, *The Enigma of the Poltergeist* (West Nyack, N.Y.: Parker, 1967), and a brief summary of the court proceedings is given in an article, "The Poltergeist Meets the Law," by Raymond Bayless, in the June 1974 issue of *Psychic* magazine. Additional material has been drawn from private files on the cases. The German court-case poltergeist is also drawn from Herbert Thurston's book cited above.

5.   BIZARRE POLTERGEISTS

The Alabama fire poltergeist was originally reported in an article, "Fire Poltergeist in Alabama?" by R. E. Hogan, in the January 1959 issue of *Fate* magazine. The Indian poltergeist recounted by A. Pillay is reprinted in Thurston, *Ghosts and Poltergeists* (cited above), and Vincent Gaddis's cases and interpretation are included in his book *Mysterious Fires and Lights* (New York: David McKay, 1967). A. R. G. Owen's views on fire poltergeists may be found in the Spring 1962 issue of *Tomorrow* magazine. The Michigan case reported by Roll and Solfvin was presented by them as a paper, "A Case of RSPK with an Epileptic Agent," at the 1975 Convention of the Parapsychological Association. The Indianapolis biting poltergeist is reviewed in Roll, *The Poltergeist* (cited above), and a more detailed analysis of the psychological factors involved in the case appears in his paper, "Poltergeist Phenomena and Interpersonal Relations," in the *Journal of the American Society for Psychical Research* 64 (1970): 66-99. The Bristol case was also recounted in Thurston's book (cited above), while the 1903 Italian water poltergeist is noted in Charles Richet, *30 Years of Psychical Research* (New York: Macmillan, 1923). The Methuen case is cited in detail in Raymond Bayless, *The Enigma of the Poltergeist* (cited above). The Minnesota case has been pieced together through several investigators who were involved with it. The Devil in Daly City case was written up in *Fate* magazine by Dr. Freda Morris as a two-part article, "Exorcising the Devil in California" (July and August 1974), and also by Alan Vaughan in "The Devil in Daly City," *Psychic* magazine, September/October 1974.

6. DEMONIC POLTERGEISTS

The Amherst case is fully covered in the *Proceedings of the American Society for Psychical Research* XIII: 89-130. Balducci's address on possession, "Parapsychology and Diabolic Possession," was printed in the *International Journal of Parapsychology* 8 (1966): 193-212. *Begone Satan!* (n.d., circa 1935) has been republished by Tan Books and Publishers (Rockford, Ill.). For the Georgetown case see the Reverend John J. Nicola, *Diabolic Possession and Exorcism* (Rockford, Ill.: Tan Books and Publishers, 1974), and "The Truth Behind

'The Exorcist,'" by Steve Erdmann, in the January 1975 issue of *Fate* magazine. For demonic possession-poltergeist cases see Leon Cristiani's *Evidence of Satan in the Modern World* (Rockford, Ill.: Tan Books and Publishers, 1974, reprint), and also Raymond Bayless, *The Enigma of the Poltergeist* (cited above.) For historical cases of religious poltergeist attacks see once again the Carrington/Fodor book, *Haunted People* (cited above), and for information on the cure of Ars's poltergeist refer to Michel de Saint Pierre, *The Remarkable Curé of Ars* (Garden City, N.Y.: Doubleday, 1963).

7.   THE INTELLIGENCE BEHIND
THE POLTERGEIST

Once again, Roll's views can be found in his own book, *The Poltergeist* (cited above). Carrington's observations are included in his *The Psychic World* (New York: Putnam, 1937). The Bishop Pike affair can be read in his book, *The Other Side* (Garden City, N.Y.: Doubleday, 1968), while Ian Stevenson's comments and cases are part of his paper, "Are Poltergeists Living or Are They Dead?" *Journal of the American Society for Psychical Research* 66 (1972): 235-252. The two out-of-the-body cases are taken from Robert Crookall, *More Astral Projections* (London: Aquarian Press, 1964) and from Celia Green, *Out-of-the-Body Experiences* (Oxford: Institute of Psychophysical Research, 1968) respectively. Dr. Tart's experiment was published in the *Journal of the American Society for Psychical Research* 62 (1968): 3-27. The Blue Harary material can be found in my previous book, *In Search of the Unknown* (New York: Taplinger, 1976), and the Landau material was published in the

Journal of the Society for Psychical Research 42. Alexandra David-Neel's encounter with the *tulpa* is chronicled in her *Magic and Mystery in Tibet* (New Hyde Park: University Books, 1958, reprint). Fodor's theory about the poltergeist is included, once again, in his and Hereward Carrington's *Haunted People* (cited above).

8. CAN WE OVERCOME THE POLTERGEIST?

Dr. John Layard's views were published as a paper, "Psi Phenomena and Poltergeists," *Proceedings of the Society for Psychical Research*, July 1944. The Baltimore poltergeist was analyzed by Fodor in his posthumous book, *Between Two Worlds* (West Nyack, N.Y.: Parker Publishing Co., 1964), and Matthew Manning describes his own poltergeist in *The Link* (New York: Holt, Rinehart and Winston, 1975). Hewat McKenzie's career and his poltergeist investigations are chronicled in Muriel Hankey's biography of him, *J. Hewat McKenzie* (New York: Garrett Publications, 1963). Dr. Rex Stanford's theories on the nature of PK are expressed in his lengthy paper, "An Experimentally Testable Model for Spontaneous Psi Events. II. Psychokinetic Events," *Journal of the American Society for Psychical Research* 68 (1974): 321-356. For Mary Williams's report on Roger, see "The Poltergeist Man" in the *International Journal of Parapsychology* 6 (1964): 424-454. Elwood Worcester's experiences were included in his book co-authored with Samuel McComb, *Body, Mind and Spirit* (New York: Charles Scribner's Sons, 1938). Benjamin Karpman presented his views on therapy in his paper, "Objective Psychotherapy," *Journal of Clinical Psychology* 5 (1949): 193-342.

Index

the Parapsychology
Foundation (1965), 205
International Institute for
Psychical Research (IIRP),
81–82, 85
*International Journal of
Parapsychology*, 50

Jaffé, 41–42
James, Mrs., 113, 116–21
James, Chris, 113–23, 259
Janet, Pierre, 217
"Jeffrey" (poltergeist), 49, 50
Johnson, James, 51
Joiner, S. H., 164
*Journal of the American
Society for Psychical
Research*, 181, 238, 239,
243
Julio (poltergeist agent),
98–105, 109, 111, 260
Jung, C. G., 32–33, 36, 162

Kamur, Sisir, 238–39
Karger, Dr. J., 128
Karin case (Sweden), 70–74,
86
Karpman, Benjamin, 279
Kaufman, Sidney W., 154,
157
King, Mrs. Charles, 172–73
Kolodny, Leo, 19

Kulagina, Nina, 18–22

Landau, Eileen and Lucian,
245–46
Langman, Mrs. W. S.,
107–108
Lassagne, Catherine, 228
Las Vegas Strip (Viewmaster
strip), 27
Laubheim, Alvin, 98–99
Laval, M., 141–42
Lawrence Eagle-Tribune, 185
Layard, Dr. John, 255–56
Lewis, E. E., 58
Link, The (Manning), 261
Lombroso, Cesare, 63–64
London *Daily Mirror*, 81
London *Sunday Pictorial*, 81
Los Angeles Times, 144, 145,
152
Losey, Chauncy P., 57
Lowe, W. M., 145, 148, 152
Lund, Reverend Mr., 96
Lynwood poltergeist, 152-58

McKenzie, J. Hewat, 269–72
Magic and Mystery in Tibet
(David-Neel), 248
Maimonides Medical Center,
17, 22, 23, 26–30, 103
Malbroun, Monastery of,
140–41

By the same author . . .

The Infinite Boundary

Spirit Possession, Madness, and Multiple Personality

Do spirits of the dead influence the living? Could some cases of mental illness be complicated by spirit obsession or actual possession?

This possibility first came to light early this century, when a Massachusetts jeweller claimed he was possessed by the spirit of R. Swain Gifford, a celebrated landscape painter. The jeweller's paintings and sketches matched unfinished and never exhibited work left by Gifford when he died, while others represented his remote island home. From the basis of this case, Professor James Hyslop spent years establishing possession as the root cause in cases of both madness and multiple personality.

Following the work of Professor Hyslop, both psychic investigators and conventional psychologists have studied the influence of psychic and paranormal factors in mental illness: Dr Titus Bull, a neurologist who cured patients by exorcizing them with the help of a Spiritualist medium; Dr Elwood Worcester, a social pioneer whose attempts to unite religion with psychology led him to confront cases of spirit possession; and Dr Walter Prince, a clergyman-turned-psychologist who cured paranoia by treating patients with exorcism. This is their story.

By drawing on much new and previously unpublished material, *The Infinite Boundary* sheds new light on our spiritual nature, the causes of psychological disorders, and their possible treatment and cure.

The Return From Silence

A Study of Near-Death Experiences

Is there life after death? For the living, this is the greatest unsolved mystery, but one for which we shall all know the answer one day. However, there are many people who have had close calls with death and who believe they have been given a glimpse of the future, of an existence which awaits us after we die. They find themselves floating outside their bodies, and often transported to a heavenly world before returning to earth. Do these near-death experiences prove that the soul survives after death, or are they simply vivid hallucinations?

The Return From Silence is an up-to-date examination of what medicine, psychology and science are learning from the near-death experience, or NDE. Rather than *assuming* that such experiences prove life after death, the author critically examines the important issues concerning the phenomenon, such as who has the experiences, how it affects them, and whether their culture affects the manner of their experience. Furthermore, can the experience be induced by situations other than near-death?

The Return From Silence offers the reader a survey and evaluation of *all* aspects of the near-death experience, the study of which can be both intellectually and spiritually rewarding, for exploring the experience of death is an exercise in living, not dying.

Beyond Reality

The Role Unseen Dimensions Play in Our Lives

Folklore and traditional occult wisdom have long acknowledged the existence of 'higher worlds' beyond our own. In this challenging and wide-ranging book D. Scott Rogo examines various 'intrusions' that take place in our reality . . . intrusions from realms beyond our sensory capabilities or from the mind itself. Rifts between daily reality and other dimensions provoke phenomena such as psychokinesis, ghosts, UFOs and religious miracles. Also studied are cases of physical objects that seem to 'pop' in and out of physical existence.

Beyond Reality goes on to cover existence beyond death — children who have 'seen' into the afterlife, people who have heard its music and cases of reincarnation in Western culture, which suggest that after we die our disembodied consciousness evolves to become a part of parallel realities. Also included is a dramatic reappraisal of UFO abduction cases, showing that these kidnappings come not from outer space but some extra dimension linked to the minds of the witnesses themselves. Lastly, the book explores religious faith and the remarkable potential of the sheer psychic power of belief.

Highlighted throughout with genuine cases drawn from the author's own investigations, this thought-provoking book will appeal to all those who are interested in exploring the mysteries of the universe.